'It's cold out

'Ain't I keeping ...
husked against her ~~left ear,~~ ...
and rather disturbingly, at the lobe.

'Stop that at once!' Verity snapped, trying desperately to ignore the delightful tingling sensation spreading down to her toes. 'Right from the start you've taken the most outrageous liberties with my person. You are no gentleman, sir!'

'Oh, I can be when I choose,' he returned blandly.

'Well, I've seen precious little evidence of it.'

Anne Ashley was born and educated in Leicester. She lives in the West Country with two cats, her two sons and a husband who has a wonderful and very necessary sense of humour. She says of this book, 'As I sit here on this rainy day, looking out of the window at my poor neglected garden which used to be my pride and joy, and see weeds flourishing where once lovely flowers used to grow, half of me curses those two handsome rogues who have taken up so much of my time in recent months, keeping me a virtual prisoner, chained to my typewriter. But the other half of me doesn't begrudge one single second. Like my spirited heroine, I fell hopelessly in love with Major Brin Carter and the Coachman, and I'm sure you'll do so too, if you read on. . .'

Recent titles by the same author:

THE NEGLECTFUL GUARDIAN
LADY LINFORD'S RETURN
THE EARL OF RAYNE'S WARD

MISS HARCOURT'S DILEMMA

Anne Ashley

MILLS & BOON®
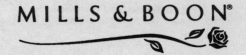

*First published in Great Britain 1998
Harlequin Mills & Boon Limited,
Eton House, 18-24 Paradise Road, Richmond, Surrey TW9 1SR*

© Anne Ashley 1998

ISBN 0 263 80786 X

*Set in Times 10 on 12 pt. by
Rowland Phototypesetting Limited
Bury St Edmunds, Suffolk*

04-9805-74434

*Printed and bound in Great Britain by
Caledonian International Book Manufacturing Ltd, Glasgow*

Chapter One

1815

It was undoubtedly the burning ambition of most well-bred young ladies of marriageable age to enjoy the heady delights of at least one London Season. Like moths to a candle's flame, they were drawn to the capital for those few short weeks each spring in the hope that at the end of the ruinously expensive social whirl, where they could mix with the Cream of Society, they would bring a gleam of satisfaction to their ambitious relatives' eyes by achieving a suitable match or, better still, an advantageous one.

So why on earth, Verity wondered, staring with scant interest through the carriage window at the passing Kentish countryside, was she journeying to the capital? She had no wish to rub shoulders with members of the top ten thousand and had absolutely no desire whatsoever to marry a member of the *ton*. She recoiled at the mere thought of ever becoming a dutiful wife and kowtowing to the whims of some well-born gentleman. So why in heaven's name had she allowed herself to be bludgeoned into agreeing to a London Season in the first place?

She could not prevent a wry little smile as she turned her head and fixed her eyes on the rather plump middle-aged widow dozing very contentedly in the opposite corner of the carriage. No one who didn't know Lady Clara Billington well would ever imagine that beneath that rather indolent but graciously charming exterior was hidden a razor-sharp manipulative mind that the most accomplished strategist would have admired.

The well-sprung carriage lurched suddenly, bringing that lady awake with a start. 'Oh, great heavens!' she exclaimed, automatically raising one podgy white hand to straighten her very fashionable bonnet. 'I dare swear this road gets worse each time I travel along it. Remind me to have a word with my brother Charles, Verity, my dear. Something really ought to be done about it.'

After making a great play of rearranging the folds of her maroon-coloured bombazine carriage dress, Lady Billington looked up to discover her niece regarding her with a disturbingly calculating gleam in her very fine eyes. 'What is the matter, my love? Why, you are looking at me as though I were a complete stranger!'

'Was I?' Like the look in her eyes, Verity's smile was not pleasant. 'As a matter of fact, I am beginning to wonder just how well I do know you, Aunt Clara. I realise, of course, that since the day I left the seminary you have been scheming to get me to London for a Season. What quite amazes me, though, is that you managed to get me to agree to it eventually!'

Lady Billington's only response to this was a rather warm but decidedly vague smile before she turned her head to stare resolutely out of the window.

In point of fact her astute young niece had been only

partially right. Almost from the day of her dear brother's sad demise Lady Billington had dreamt of chaperoning his sole offspring for the duration of at least one London Season. She had not been blessed with children of her own, and had taken a keen interest in all her nieces and nephews, but Verity had quickly become her undoubted favourite. When Verity's mother had sold her Hampshire home and had returned to her native Yorkshire to keep house for her unmarried elder brother, Mr Lucius Redmond, Lady Billington had kept in contact with her sister-in-law and niece, corresponding regularly and visiting at least once a year.

When Verity's mother, too, had sadly and most unexpectedly passed away, Lady Billington had been slightly hurt to discover that Lucius had been entrusted with Verity's sole guardianship. However, being a bachelor, Mr Redmond had been more than willing to listen to her views on the rearing of a young girl, who had sadly been allowed to degenerate into something of a tomboy by her doting parent, and it had been at Lady Billington's instigation that Verity had been sent to a very select seminary in Bath.

Thankfully, by the age of sixteen, when Verity had left the school, she had outgrown her tomboyish ways and had blossomed into an exceedingly lovely young lady. Not only had she an exquisite figure and a delicately featured face, but she had been blessed with the deepest of deep blue eyes, made more striking by a riot of blue-black curls. Sadly, though, she seemed impervious to the gifts Mother Nature had so generously bestowed upon her and, apart from the occasional visit she had made to Lady Billington's home in Kent, had been more than happy to incarcerate herself in Yorkshire, helping her uncle to run his very successful newspaper business.

'That air of innocence doesn't fool me for a moment, Aunt Clara,' Verity stated flatly, breaking the silence which had lengthened between them. 'You are a devious, conniving woman! You know full well that had you not intimated that you were no longer going to send me those juicy snippets of information, which I find so invaluable, I wouldn't be sitting here now.'

'Unjust, child!' Lady Billington countered with as much vehemence as a lady of her placid disposition could muster. 'I merely wrote and told you that with that wretched Corsican upstart on the loose again, and half of Society on the Continent, there would be little enough going on in London worth mentioning and that it would be far better for you to accompany me to the capital this year so that together we might just hear enough items of gossip for you to write an interesting little piece about the Season.'

Verity was far from convinced, but decided that it was not in her own best interest to comment further, for she was very well aware that without her aunt's invaluable help she would never have been able to write those articles for inclusion in her uncle's newspaper.

He had been very much against the idea at first, not wanting to sully his journal with, as he termed it, 'a load of frivolous gossip', but when Verity had argued that it was not only men who read newspapers, and that an occasional article of interest to the fair sex would be much appreciated by his many female readers, her uncle had allowed her to have her way. He was old-fashioned enough, however, to believe that ladies of Verity's class had no business working at all, and had stipulated right from the start that her efforts would be an occasional feature and had limited her to just one article per month.

Verity had been more than satisfied with that. Her items on fashions, the latest way to dress one's hair and the most up-to-date beauty aids had proved of immense interest to the ladies of Yorkshire, but most popular of all had been her résumé on the events of the London Season, for which, of course, she had needed the ever-watchful Lady Billington to forward the gossip about those more colourful and well-known leaders of fashion.

'Well, if London is thin of company this Season,' Verity remarked, her finely arched black brows drawing together in thought, 'there is always Prinny to fall back on. He never fails to indulge in some lunacy, and I'm sure not every member of the top ten thousand has deserted our shores for the delights of Vienna. . . Or is it Brussels they are all flocking to now?'

'Yes, I believe it is. A pity, really.' Lady Billington gave a sudden start. 'I *have* heard one item of gossip whilst I've been in Kent which should interest you. It looks as though Arthur Brinley's grandson is destined to be the next Viscount Dartwood.' There was no response to this and she regarded her niece in silence for a moment. 'I know how fond you were of that old man, Verity, but I cannot recall your ever mentioning his grandson. Surely you are acquainted with Major Carter?'

'I knew him, yes,' Verity admitted, 'but I haven't set eyes on him for. . .oh, must be over five years now.'

Once again Lady Billington studied her niece's lovely profile in silence for a moment, then said, 'Am I right in thinking that you do not care for the Major very much, my dear? Do you hold him in dislike?'

Dislike. . .? The word seemed to echo round the confines of the carriage, bringing a further thoughtful frown to crease Verity's forehead. Did she dislike Arthur Brinley's grandson? No, she didn't think so, even though he had hurt her rather badly once, but that seemed such a long time ago. If she had thought about him at all in recent years, which hadn't been often, it had been when she had read a report in her uncle's newspaper of his exploits during the Peninsular Campaign.

A sigh escaped her. 'No, I don't dislike him, Aunt Clara, even though he is a nincompoop.' She shrugged. 'I really ought, I suppose, to think well of him, for he has proved himself a very courageous soldier. . . And he did once save my life.'

'Great heavens!' Lady Billington was astounded. 'What on earth happened?'

'Oh, nothing very exciting,' Verity responded with a dismissive wave of her hand. 'I came perilously close to drowning myself once—would most certainly have succeeded in doing so had not Brin dived into that lake to rescue me.'

Her aunt shuddered. 'I suppose that occurred in the days when you indulged in your tomboyish behaviour?'

'It most certainly did,' Verity confirmed, completely unabashed by her aunt's rather disapproving tone. She gave a sudden start. 'But you're right, you know! Brin's coming into the title will prove of immense interest to the ladies of Yorkshire. He's quite the local hero. It's rumoured that he's sold his commission.' Her lovely eyes narrowed speculatively. 'He hasn't returned to Yorkshire. At least,' she amended, 'he hadn't when I left last week. . .I wonder where he's hiding himself?'

'He may very well be in London, dear. It's rumoured that uncle of his is deteriorating fast, and although the dreadful creature has done everything humanly possible

to stop his nephew from coming into the title by marrying
that poor child who's young enough to be his grand-
daughter, as I've mentioned before, it looks very likely
the Major will very shortly be the new Viscount
Dartwood.'

Verity gurgled with unholy amusement. 'Poor Brin! If
he has been foolish enough to descend on the capital,
he'll have every matchmaking mama after him.'

Lady Billington cast her niece a mildly reproachful
look, and was about to inform her that she had a rather
perverse sense of humour when there was a most peculiar
splintering sound. The next instant she was thrown
against the side of the carriage as the equipage came to
a rather unexpected and abrupt halt.

'What on earth has happened?'

'I've no idea,' Verity responded, having managed to
keep her seat by retaining a firm grasp on the strap,
'but here's Ridge now, so no doubt we'll soon discover
what's amiss.'

The off-side door was wrenched open and the worried
face of Lady Billington's head groom appeared in the
aperture. 'Are you all right, my lady?'

'Yes, Ridge. We're both fine,' she assured him whilst
trying to ease herself into a more upright position, which
was no easy task as the carriage was leaning at a most
peculiar angle. 'What on earth has happened?'

'The front near-side wheel's damaged and one of the
traces is broke. Luckily we're within sight of Sit-
tingbourne, ma'am. If you would care to travel in t'other
carriage to The Crown, me and Clem'll walk the 'orses
to the inn, and then I'll see about getting the damage
repaired. Mind, there's every chance it won't be today.'

'Oh, how very tiresome! I did so want to reach London

in good time to attend Lady Swayle's party this evening. Still—' she shrugged '—it cannot be helped. If you would assist Miss Verity, and then help me to alight.'

Being young and slender, Verity had little trouble in scrambling out, but Lady Billington, whose girth had increased greatly in middle age, found the task no easy one, and it took the combined efforts of both niece and groom to ease her out of the carriage and onto the road.

The second coach, which had drawn to a halt a few yards behind, was not only piled high with baggage, for Lady Billington had never been known to travel light, but contained her personal maid, Dodd, the butler and what Verity considered two of the most obnoxious pets in Christendom: a green parrot and an overfed lap-dog called Horace.

Pandemonium broke out when Verity, in her usual no-nonsense manner, scooped Horace off the seat and deposited him on the hapless butler's lap. The pampered Pekinese, having taken exception to being rudely awoken from his slumber, voiced his displeasure by alternately growling and yapping which, in turn, startled the excitable parrot into vocal outbursts, and its disharmonious ear-piercing squawks continued unabated until the carriage came to a halt in the inn yard.

'That is it!' Verity snapped, alighting almost before the groom had let down the steps. 'I refuse to travel another mile with those repulsive pets of yours. Why on earth you find it necessary to take the noisy blighters with you whenever you travel, I'll never know!'

'Now, now, dear, calm down,' Lady Billington said soothingly, following her irate young niece into the inn. 'I don't know from where you get that naughty temper of yours. Your dear papa was the most placid of creatures and I can never recall witnessing your mama ever lose her cool. Although. . .' she frowned suddenly '. . .some of the Harcourts have been known to have had a short fuse. Your great-grandfather, the fourth Duke, was a man of almost insane temper. I recall several members of the family remarking that he ought to have been locked up in Bedlam.'

Verity cast her a glance of impatience. 'There's a difference between insanity and justifiable annoyance, Aunt Clara. Those confounded pets of yours are enough to try the patience of a saint! And if you try to force me to travel the rest of the way to London in the same carriage as those two monsters you'll risk losing them both, for I shan't balk at wringing that green goose's neck or at throwing that pampered whelp out of the window!'

Lady Billington wisely refrained from lecturing her niece on the unforgivable wickedness of hurting dumb creatures, and said instead, 'But, dear, you cannot possibly remain here by yourself. Why, it's unthinkable!'

'I shan't be by myself. Ridge will be with me. Look,' she went on hurriedly, not giving her aunt the opportunity to point out the very obvious flaw in this scheme, 'let us have some light refreshments whilst we're waiting for Ridge to discover if the carriage can be repaired today, and then decide what we're going to do when we've spoken to him again.'

As this was the most sensible course of action Lady Billington caught the attention of one of the inn servants and ordered a light repast. They repaired to the coffee-room and occupied their time while waiting for Ridge by watching the comings and goings of the numerous travellers moving about the very busy coaching inn. When Ridge finally came to them his tidings were not good. The carriage, it seemed, could not be repaired until the morning, so he suggested he put up at the inn and continue the journey to London the following day, once repairs had been effected.

Lady Billington had no fault to find with these arrangements, and summoned the landlord, but when Verity announced that she too would remain for the night and travel with Ridge the following day, Lady Billington's sense of propriety was deeply offended and she simply could not countenance such a scheme.

'I'm sorry, Verity, but it is out of the question. Why, it's unthinkable that you remain here without so much as a maid! I'm afraid you have no choice but to continue the journey with me.'

'No!' Verity argued, stubborn to the last. 'I won't travel with those wretched creatures!' She noticed Ridge's lips twitch slightly, and didn't miss the unmistakable look of sympathy in his eyes either, before she turned to the landlord, who was patiently waiting to hear whether one or two rooms would be required. 'Is it possible to hire a vehicle from here?'

'Ordinarily, miss, yes, it would be. But this be a busy time o' year, with folk travelling to London for the Season, and I've nothing available. Although. . .' he ran a hand over his balding pate '. . .you might just get a seat on the mail. Mind, as your name ain't on the waybill there's no guarantee, but if there be room the coachman just might take you up.'

'But you still cannot possibly travel without some female companion,' her aunt put in before Verity could voice her whole-hearted approval of this solution. 'And it's of no use your asking Dodd to accompany you because, as this good man has so rightly pointed out, there's no guarantee you'll get seats on the mail. Besides, I'll need Dodd to dress me for the party tonight.'

'Well, ma'am, I might just be able to 'elp you out there,' the landlord remarked unexpectedly, much to Verity's delight and her aunt's intense irritation. 'My young niece be awaiting the mail.' He gestured towards a corner table at which a young woman, wearing a grey cloak and bonnet, sat quite alone. 'She were in service with the Dowager Lady Longbourne, but the old lady passed on a month back and my niece be going to London to look for another position.'

Lady Billington was still far from happy over Verity's travelling to London on the mail-coach, but, after exchanging a few words with the innkeeper's niece, who seemed a very quiet and well-mannered young person, she very reluctantly acquiesced to the scheme and, as the afternoon was well advanced, wasted no further time in resuming her journey.

Once Verity had seen her aunt safely on her way, she went back inside the hostelry and sat herself down beside the innkeeper's niece. 'I suppose I ought to introduce myself as my company has been rather forced upon you,' she remarked with her friendly smile. 'My name is Harcourt. . . Verity Harcourt.'

'Margaret Jones, miss. But everyone calls me Meg.'

Verity subjected her fellow traveller to a swift appraising glance. Although dressed in sensible rather than fashionable attire, she was as neat as wax. 'So, Meg, you are journeying to the capital in the hope of finding employment?'

'Yes, miss. My sister lives there, so I'll stay with her until I can find myself another situation. I have a reference from Lady Longbourne's family. I was her ladyship's personal maid, but I don't expect I'll find work as an abigail. There are plenty with far more experience than me, so I'll be happy to take anything, for there's nothing round these parts.'

Verity subjected the innkeeper's niece to a further appraising stare. Although she was quietly spoken, and evidently a little shy in the company of strangers, her clear grey eyes looked directly at one when she spoke, and Verity rather liked that.

She turned her head to stare sightlessly across the coffee-room, wondering whether to offer the young woman employment. Having always enlisted the help of one of her uncle's female servants whenever the need had arisen, Verity had never felt it necessary to employ an experienced personal maid. However, as dear Aunt Clara was so fond of reminding her, what prevailed in the wilds of Yorkshire was not necessarily acceptable in a more polished society.

She was also very well aware that her freedom would be drastically curtailed during her time in London. Jaunting about on her own would be strictly forbidden, she knew, and it was hardly fair to expect one of her aunt's servants to bear her company whenever she wished to go out for a walk, nor was it reasonable to suppose that Dodd would be willing to tend to her needs for the duration of her stay as well as those of Lady Billington.

As was her wont, Verity came to a decision swiftly. 'How would you like to work for me, Meg?' she enquired, and then chuckled at the young woman's look of astonishment. 'Truly, I am in earnest,' she assured her. 'It's high time I had a personal maid. Although I think it only fair to warn you that I live for the most part in Yorkshire, so if a quiet life in the country is not to your taste it might be best if you did seek a situation in the capital.'

'Oh, no, miss. I was born and raised in the country, and Lady Longbourne never travelled far from home when I worked for her,' Meg hurriedly assured her, hardly daring to believe her great good fortune. 'No, it isn't that. It's just... Well, won't the lady who was with you earlier want to speak to me first? Your aunt, wasn't it?'

'Yes, Lady Billington is my aunt, but it has little to do with her, even though we shall be residing in her town house for the next few weeks. No, it's my guardian who'll be paying your wages. And Uncle Lucius will adhere to my decision, I'm sure.'

'In that case, miss,' Meg responded, rising from the table just as the unmistakable sound of a horn was heard heralding the arrival of the mail, 'I'd better have a word with my uncle. If you aren't able to get a seat on the coach then it's my duty now to stay with you.'

A few minutes later Verity watched a tall man stride purposefully into the inn by way of a side entrance. His powerful frame was swathed in a voluminous, caped grey cloak. An old-fashioned tricorn was pulled low over his brow and the lower part of his face was muffled in a dark woollen scarf so that only his eyes were visible. She assumed he must be the coachman, for he went directly across to the innkeeper and then, after exchanging a few words with Meg and her uncle, turned his head in her direction. He stared across at her for what seemed an interminable and, to her way of thinking, quite unnecessary length of time before giving an almost imperceptible nod of his head and then strode through the doorway by which he had entered.

'Yes, it's all right, Miss Harcourt,' Meg came across to inform her. 'The Coachman said he'd take you up, but we'd best hurry because he's a little behind schedule.'

As Verity could see no sign of her aunt's groom, she asked the innkeeper to inform Ridge that she had managed to get a seat on the mail and then went outside to the inn yard to find the coach, painted in the royal livery of scarlet, maroon and black, ready and waiting to leave.

'What, no baggage, lass? I 'ope I ain't taking up no runaway!'

Momentarily startled, Verity looked up to see the Coachman peering down at her from his seat on the box. She gained the distinct impression from the wicked glint in his light brown eyes that he was laughing at her, but tactfully refrained from giving him a well-deserved set-down in case he should take umbrage and then refuse to take her. She merely contented herself with a haughty toss of her proud little head before clambering inside the rather musty-smelling equipage.

Thankfully the coach was not too crowded. A rather plump lady holding a sleeping infant on her lap, a man in rough workman's clothes, who bore all the appearance of a farmer, and a middle-aged individual of below average height, dressed in a suit of severe black cloth, occupied one seat, and Verity sat herself beside Meg on the other. Apart from a cursory glance she took little heed of her fellow travellers and began to chat away to Meg as the coach pulled out of the inn yard, telling her of her uncle's lovely home situated on the edge of the moors, and of the plans her aunt had made for the forthcoming Season.

'However,' Verity went on to say, 'with the unexpected turn of events in Europe my aunt doesn't envisage such a gay time in London this year, so with any luck she will not wish to remain until June.'

'Ha! You speak of—how do you English say?—the Upstart's escape from Elba, no?' the man in the black suit unexpectedly remarked in a decidedly foreign accent, drawing all eyes in his direction.

'Oh, my gawd!' ejaculated the fat woman, suddenly holding the sleeping infant more tightly to her ample bosom. 'Never tell me you're one of them there 'eathen Frenchies!'

'No, *madame*. I am Swiss and have papers to prove it. I am a watchmaker by trade,' he went on to divulge, tapping the flat wooden box resting on his lap, 'and am in your country on business.'

'No doubt you had started upon your travels before news of the Emperor's escape had reached your home town, *monsieur*?' Verity remarked, unable to prevent a smile at the way the fat lady continued to regard the gentleman with blatant suspicion.

'Yes, *mademoiselle*, otherwise I would not have ventured forth, I assure you. But—' he shrugged '—I am in no danger here, I think.'

'Indeed you are not, *monsieur*. We can safely put our trust in Wellington. He will not fail us,' Verity assured him, a hint of pride creeping in to her voice, before turning once again to Meg, who was beginning to lose much of her shyness with her new and, what seemed to her, pleasantly friendly young mistress.

The miles sped by while Verity and Meg chatted away contentedly, and before they knew it they were drawing up in the yard of yet another busy posting house. The change of horses was effected quickly, and then they were on their way again.

It was a well-known fact that nothing was allowed to hinder mail-coaches. The guard would sound his horn to warn toll-keepers of their approach so that gates were opened without the need to stop. It came as something of a surprise to all the passengers, therefore, when for no apparent reason the coach slowed down and came to an unexpected halt.

Verity noticed the rather apprehensive glance the Swiss gentleman cast out of the window before he turned his rather hard grey eyes in her direction.

'What can be wrong, *mademoiselle*?'

Her shrug betrayed her complete lack of interest. She was in no particular hurry to reach London, so was not unduly concerned with any possible delay. She could hear the sound of voices outside and assumed that someone had flagged down the coach, possibly to warn the driver of some hazard ahead. No more than a minute or two had elapsed before they set off again, but at a much slower pace, and then, after travelling no more than a few hundred yards, they came to a halt yet again in the yard of a small wayside inn. Moments later the off-side door was thrown wide and the guard in his scarlet and gold livery appeared in the aperture.

'There's a tree fallen across the road half a mile or so ahead and vehicles building up quite some way back from it, so we'll be waiting 'ere until the road's been cleared. The Coachman says if you wants a bite to eat, make the most of the time now, 'cause he won't be stopping again 'cepting to change 'orses.'

'An excellent suggestion!' Verity remarked, cutting across the fat lady's grumbles as she accepted the guard's helping hand to alight. 'No one can be held responsible for what is, after all, an act of God.'

'Glad t'discover tha's a sensible lass. Mayhap tha's no runaway after all,' that goading, thickly-accented voice from above once again remarked, causing Verity to miss her footing. She caught the heel of her shoe in the hem of her skirts and would have fallen down the steps but for the guard's supporting hand.

'Now see what you've made me do!' she snapped, glancing down at the torn flounce before raising angrily accusing dark blue eyes up to those of the Coachman. 'And I would be grateful if in the future you kept your inane reflections to yourself!'

Meg and the Coachman's wickedly taunting deep rumble of masculine laughter followed Verity into the inn. Like most volatile people, she had a temper quickly roused, but it just as swiftly abated, and she had never been known to vent her ill-humour on anyone other than the person who had instigated her wrath. So, when Meg tentatively offered to pin up the torn flounce, she thanked her but said she could manage perfectly well and then politely asked her to see about getting them some refreshments.

Apart from the mail-coach passengers there was only one other customer in the inn, a thickset man of average height, supping a tankard of ale as he stared resolutely out of the window, but even so Verity was far too modest to raise her skirts and effect temporary repairs to her torn undergarment whilst in the presence of the opposite sex, and so looked about for somewhere a little more private.

The inn was only small, and there appeared to be no private parlour, but she noticed a passageway leading off the tap and succeeded in slipping away without being noticed. As luck would have it the first door along the passageway was slightly ajar and she didn't hesitate to poke her head into the room. Thankfully it was deserted, but there were the remains of a meal on the table and, more importantly, there was a large screen placed halfway across the window which, Verity noticed as she secreted herself behind it, had been so positioned to try to prevent the considerable draught blasting through the ill-fitting windows from penetrating too far into the room.

She had just completed her task, and was placing the spare pins back into her reticule, when she heard the sound of heavy footsteps as someone entered the room. She had never suffered from shyness, not even as a child, so it would not have embarrassed her in the least to show herself and explain the very understandable reason for her presence in the room. Yet, without quite knowing why, she decided not to do so.

Peering through the crack in the screen, Verity saw a man with his back towards her, standing by the grate. She had not seen his face earlier, and she still couldn't see it now, but she had no difficulty in recognising him as the man who had been staring fixedly through the taproom window when she had first entered the inn. He was dressed in outdoor clothes, so it was safe to assume that he must be on the point of departure, she thought, but when, after several minutes had elapsed, he continued to stare down with apparent rapt interest at the logs burning brightly on the hearth she decided to make her presence known.

Reaching for her reticule, which she had placed on the rather worm-eaten windowsill, Verity was about to step out from behind the screen when she heard someone else enter the room, and an unmistakable foreign-accented voice say, 'It was very clever of you, *monsieur*, to meet me here. How could you have possibly known we would be making this unscheduled stop?'

'You're not the only one with brains,' the other man responded in deep, rather harsh-sounding tones, which betrayed both irritation and resentment. 'I arrived early at the meeting place and learned of the tree blocking the road. It's possible for a man on horseback to get through, so I decided to ride on ahead. Mail-coaches are famed for keeping good time. I guessed the Coachman wouldn't be stopping again, except to change horses, and this place is only about half a mile away from the blockage. I was looking out for you from the window, intending to follow the rest of the way to London in the hope that I might just get the chance to pass on my master's message.'

Verity, having placed her eye to the crack in the screen again, had a perfect view of the foreigner and watched his thin lips twist into the most unpleasant and sinister smile. She had paid only scant attention to him in the coach, accepting him completely at face value. Now, however, she was far from sure that he was all that he seemed. There was something decidedly calculating in those hard grey eyes of his. He began speaking again and she listened intently.

'How obliging it was, then, of the Coachman to pull in here.' His unpleasant smile faded. 'We have little time and it would not be wise, I think, to be seen together. Have you anything for me?'

'Nothing yet. But my master will meet you at the usual rendezvous on Friday evening at eight o'clock.'

'Ah, yes! I remember. The inn at zee Leetle, Leetle Frampington. You English are so *drôle*, *n'est-ce-pas*? Very well. Inform your master I shall be there. And remind him the situation is of the most urgent. I must not delay. My beloved Emperor needs that information. He must know Wellington's plans!'

Chapter Two

Verity had always felt justifiably proud of the noble Harcourt blood flowing through her veins. Like any other family it had certainly produced the odd black sheep, the usual smattering of rogues and rakes. The most notorious had been the third Duke, who had been suspected of murdering his first wife, although it had to be said in his defence that this had never been proved, but even those whose names were never mentioned except in whispers had always been unfailingly loyal to the crown.

Three of her young cousins were engaged in the present conflict with France, and, had Verity been born a boy, she wouldn't have hesitated to take the King's Shilling. She had never lacked for courage or daring, a circumstance which had caused Lady Billington many sleepless nights, so it would have come as something of a surprise to that lady to know that it was as much as Verity could do to stop her knees from buckling in those moments when she watched the foreigner, quickly followed by his accomplice, leave the room.

The Emperor. . .? Wellington. . .? The words seemed to reverberate off the walls like so many hammer-blows.

Dear Lord! What had she inadvertently stumbled upon? More importantly, what on earth should she do about it?

Her first impulse was to confront the foreigner, to accuse him of being a spy and have him placed in the hands of the authorities, but she curbed it. There was a very good chance she might not be believed, and truth to tell she could hardly believe it herself. It would be her word against his, after all, and no doubt he carried authentic-looking enough documents stating that he was nothing more than the innocent Swiss watchmaker he purported to be. Then, of course, there was that other man to consider. Her eyes narrowed as she recalled his words. Evidently he was merely the go-between, nothing more than a servant. But if she could get a close look at his face, and pass on an accurate description of the man to the authorities, he just might lead them to his master, the real villain of the piece.

Her course of action now clear, Verity tried to step out from her hiding place once again, only to be thwarted this time by a slatternly maidservant, whose apron was streaked with grime and whose dishevelled hair looked as though it had not seen a comb in a month of Sundays. In silent dismay she watched as the servant began, with a lassitude that was painful to witness, to pile the used dishes onto a tray. If the innkeeper had given instructions for the table to be cleared then it stood to reason that the go-between had paid his shot and was on the point of departure. There was not a moment to lose, but there was little Verity could do. It was of vital importance now that no one knew of her presence in this room, and so she had, perforce, to wait until the maidservant had withdrawn.

It seemed to take an eternity for the girl to complete

her task, but the instant the coast was clear Verity wasted
not a second in returning to the entrance to the tap. She
had a clear view of the counter, where the mail-coach
guard stood beside the passenger who bore all the appearance of a farmer. She could also see the plump lady
sitting at the corner table, feeding broth to her infant,
and she could just make out the rim of her newly
appointed maid's grey bonnet.

Meg was seated at the table by a substantial wooden
pillar, and looked to be speaking to someone outside
Verity's field of vision. In all probability it was the
foreign spy, but Verity wasn't unduly concerned over
this. Meg, after all, had no notion of his true profession
and would, therefore, behave quite naturally. But of the
go-between there was no sign. Might he have departed
already?

Picking up her skirts, Verity ran back along the passageway to the door at the far end. As she had suspected
it led outside to the stable yard. Since their arrival at the
inn the light had deteriorated. The sky now was heavily
overcast, but there was sufficient light for her to see all
the outbuildings quite clearly and for her to avoid the
numerous puddles, the residue of the previous day's tor-
rential downpour, dotted across the yard as she made her
way towards the stable block.

The place appeared deserted. The only sounds she
detected were those made by the coach horses champing
at their bits, but as she drew level with the mail-coach,
brought to a halt a matter of a few yards from the stable
entrance, she detected a sudden movement towards
the rear of the carriage and turned her head to see the
Coachman, his back towards her, staring fixedly out
across the open countryside as he inhaled on a cheroot.

He seemed oblivious to her presence, and as Verity was more than content to keep it that way she tiptoed across the remaining distance to the large stable only to find it, frustratingly, empty.

'And what be you about, lass, skulking out 'ere?'

Verity gave a start and swung round to see the tall figure of the Coachman standing in the doorway, effectively blocking her exit. She regarded him in exasperated silence. He really was the most irritating creature she had ever had the misfortune to encounter!

'Do you get some perverse pleasure from creeping up behind innocent damsels and scaring them half out of their wits?' she enquired, with all the haughtiness of her noble Harcourt blood.

He flicked the stub of his cheroot into a convenient puddle down by his left boot before folding his arms across his broad chest and casting his eyes over her with a slow insolence which infuriated her. 'I'm beginning to wonder just 'ow innocent tha be, lass. And I can't 'elp wondering what tha be doing travelling by the mail.'

Verity had grown accustomed over the years to receiving every respect and courtesy from menials, but this individual was a law unto himself. What business was it of his how she chose to travel about the country? The mannerless creature really ought to be reminded of his proper place, she decided, but the masterly set-down which rose in her throat was held in check by a sudden thought.

'How long have you been out here? Did you happen to notice a man in a grey cloak, not unlike your own, leave the inn?'

'Ha! So I were right! Tha's a runaway, after all, and thy lover's deserted you.'

'Don't be nonsensical!' Verity was fast coming to the end of her tether, and only just managed to control the overwhelming desire to box his ears soundly. 'I have neither the time nor the inclination to bandy words with you. Now, just answer my question, dolt!'

'Dolt, is it?' he remarked, an unmistakable edge sharpening his not unattractive deep, husky voice, and before Verity could do anything to avoid him, he had bridged the distance between them in three massive strides and had picked her up in his strong arms.

Much to her further outrage, her demands to be put down at once were sublimely ignored, and the next instant she found herself tossed unceremoniously down on a pile of hay with the Coachman's body pressed half on top of her, effectively keeping her there. More scandalised than afraid, she hit out with her small fists, only to have her wrists captured effortlessly and imprisoned above her head in one large hand. She had a glimpse of thick, slightly waving hair as the Coachman turned his head away and tossed his hat aside. Then his other hand was placed over her eyes and a firm, warm mouth was clamped over hers, silencing her angry threat of reprisals.

Only then did Verity experience a pulsating throb of fear tremble its way through her as her aunt's dire warnings of never permitting herself to be alone with a man echoed tauntingly in her ears. Now she could appreciate that sage advice, for she was brutally aware that she lacked the strength to stop this assault upon her——but equally aware that her captor was exerting only sufficient force to hold her firm. Her breasts were in no danger of being crushed beneath that broad expanse of chest, her wrists were not likely to suffer harm from that merely restraining hold, nor was her mouth in the least peril of

becoming bruised beneath the featherlight touch of lips
that parted hers with infinitely gentle expertise.

Never before had she found herself in such a comprom-
ising position. Never before had any man dared to take
such liberties with her. She knew she ought to feel dis-
gusted and outraged, and yet she seemed powerless to
prevent her lips trembling invitingly in response when
his kiss deepened. His mouth fitted so perfectly to hers
that it seemed almost as if they had become as one, that
she belonged to him just as surely as if they had been
legally joined in wedlock, and she only knew in those
moments of newly awakened desire that she didn't want
those pleasurable sensations tingling through her ever
to end.

Well, now, lass, yon were right revealing.' In one swift
movement he had pulled away from her and had the
muffler covering his face even before Verity had a chance
to open her eyes. 'Ne'er bin kissed afore, and enjoyed
the experience, I'm thinking.'

His taunting was like a slap in the face, bringing her
back to reality with a cruel jolt. Scrambling to her feet,
she experienced hurt and humiliation, anger and disgust
in equal measures.

'How dare you use me like a—a trollop?' she snapped,
doing her best to brush the clinging bits of hay from her
skirts. 'I shall report you to your superiors!'

It was an empty threat, spoken only in an attempt to
conceal confusion and humiliation, she knew, and so,
seemingly, did he, for his only response was to roar with
laughter as he turned his back towards her and leaned
forward on his knees to reach his tricorn.

Verity's eyes glinted dangerously. A sudden thirst for
revenge was all-consuming and the target presented just

a mite too tempting to ignore. So, drawing back her stoutly shod foot, she placed a well-aimed and punishing kick to the seat of his breeches, the force of which sent the Coachman sprawling forward into the hay.

'Why, tha little. . .!' Wait 'til I gets 'old o' thee!'

But Verity had no intention of waiting. One confrontation with this obnoxious creature was enough to last a lifetime! She ran out of the stable and across the yard as swiftly as her young legs would carry her, and didn't stop running until she had re-entered the tap, where Meg looked up at her in some concern.

'Why, Miss Verity! Wherever have you been? I was just about to go searching for you.'

With a praiseworthy attempt at appearing nonchalant Verity seated herself at the table. 'Really, Meg, I'm deeply grateful to think that you're so concerned over my welfare,' she remarked, intentionally not lowering her voice so that the so-called watchmaker at the next table could not help but overhear, 'but there are certain times during the day when I demand privacy, and certain places where modesty dictates I must go alone. And one of those places is to be found outside in the yard.'

The explanation for her long absence appeared to satisfy both listeners: Meg looked as though she had been dipping into the rouge-pot, and the foreigner coughed delicately before picking up his glass of wine.

This was a golden opportunity to hold the Swiss gentleman, if indeed he was Swiss, in conversation, but Verity remained frustratingly in two minds. If she suddenly began to show a keen interest in her fellow traveller might he not become suspicious? Added to which, honesty prompted her to admit that she felt unequal to the task of asking seemingly innocent questions just at the moment. Having nowhere near recovered from the rather unnerving episode in the stable, she hadn't sufficient wits about her to indulge in some cat-and-mouse game. On the other hand, though, she felt it her duty to discover all she could about this man.

As it happened, the decision of how to proceed was taken out of her hands, for no sooner had she finished her now tepid cup of coffee than the guard came over to inform them that the blockage in the road had been cleared and that they would be leaving immediately.

Deliberately keeping her eyes lowered, Verity mounted the steps into the equipage, but she instinctively knew that the Coachman was staring down at her, and was no doubt deriving much amusement from her obvious discomfiture. Curse him! She knew, too, the instant they recommenced their journey, that he was deliberately tooling the vehicle at a wildly dangerous pace so as to make the ride as uncomfortable as possible. . .especially for her!

She clung to the strap as though her very life depended upon it, wondering how, with the exception of Meg, her fellow-travellers could doze while being jolted about in such a fashion. Even the 'watchmaker' had his eyes closed, and, frustratingly, they remained so, which effectively prevented Verity from trying to discover anything further about him that might have been of some use to the authorities. Consequently, by the time they had arrived in London, late in the evening, she was not in the best of humours.

After requesting Meg to secure a hackney carriage, Verity was about to alight herself when she realised she had left her reticule behind. By the time she had located its whereabouts, wedged down the side of the seat, all the other passengers had alighted. Cursing under her breath, for she had wanted to keep an eye on that spy to see in which direction he went, she turned, and was about to place her foot down on the steps when she saw the Coachman, not the guard, waiting to offer a helping hand. His eyes were sparkling with devilment which, in turn, ignited an ominous glint in her own. She had borne much that day, especially from him, and the rein on her temper finally snapped.

'I shall take leave to inform you that you are the most uncouth oaf it has ever been my misfortune to encounter! And, what is more, the most cow-handed driver ever to take up the ribbons!' she informed him with brutal frankness while resisting quite beautifully the strong urge to slap his outstretched hand away. 'Now, kindly remove your unprepossessing carcass out of my sight!'

His goading response, as it had been earlier, was to throw his head back and roar with laughter. Then, before Verity could formulate something else cutting to say, he placed his hands on her narrow waist and lifted her out of the coach, holding her effortlessly high in the air for several seconds, just as though she weighed no more than a child, before lowering her to her feet.

'Aye, tha's grow into a right floutersome lass, Verity 'Arcourt. And I mind tha'll suit me right well.'

'You think I'd. . .? Well, of all the brass-faced impertinence!'

Verity swung her arm in a wide arc, but by exercising some very neat footwork the Coachman avoided the reticule making contact with his left ear, and Verity had to content herself with a further lofty toss of the head before stalking away across the yard, the Coachman's taunting laughter, for what seemed the umpteenth time that day, ringing in her ears.

'Did you happen to notice which way that foreigner went, Meg?' she asked, after having looked in vain about the yard for him.

'No, miss. I didn't. I were busy hiring this here hackney carriage.'

Knowing that it would be rather futile to try searching for him in London's busy streets, Verity gave her aunt's address to the driver and then clambered into the hired carriage.

'That dratted Coachman!' she snapped, blaming him entirely for foiling her attempts to keep track of the spy. 'If I were a vindictive person I wouldn't think twice about reporting that oaf to his superiors. Did you see the wretch manhandling me just now?'

Meg had indeed witnessed her young mistress being assisted from the mail-coach. 'He were a bit saucy, miss,' she responded, failing completely to suppress a chuckle. 'And very taken with you he were, too.'

'I'll give him taken with me. Such impudence! Why, if the wretch ever crosses my path again, I'll. . .' Verity sat bolt-upright, gaping in astonished incredulity. 'Meg, he knows me! He knew my name.'

'Course he did, miss. I told him it, back at my uncle's inn.'

'No, Meg. We've met before today. I'd swear to it. He's a Yorkshireman. That accent of his wasn't false.' Her eyes narrowed as she turned her head to stare blindly out of the carriage window. 'Who on earth can he be?'

Chapter Three

Although Lady Billington would have been the first to admit that she was not one to bestir herself unduly, she had never been known to partake of breakfast in bed when she had a guest residing under her roof. None the less, when she entered the small breakfast parlour the following morning her motive for doing so was not primarily to bear her niece company for the first meal of the day but to take her roundly to task on the sheer folly of impulsively engaging servants without even so much as checking the authenticity of their references first.

Verity listened to the moderately staunchly voiced criticisms with equanimity. However, when her aunt paused to sip her coffee, she remarked in a tone bordering on the indifferent, 'But didn't you read Meg's reference? I asked her last night to ensure that you got it. I felt certain you would have known Lady Longbourne, or known of her. You seem to know everyone.'

'Yes, I knew her—vaguely. And, yes, Dodd did hand it to me first thing this morning and everything seems to be in order,' she freely admitted, but was still far from appeased. 'That doesn't alter the fact, though, that you hadn't taken the trouble to look at it yourself before offering the girl employment. You're so impulsive, child! It was against my better judgement that I left you yesterday. I cannot tell you what agonies I suffered! Why, anything might have happened to you!'

Something most definitely had, Verity mused, biting into a deliciously warm buttered roll, her mind going back to the previous day when she had entered that wayside inn. Then her aunt began speaking again and she forced herself to listen, but without any degree of real interest, to what she was saying.

'. . .and I learned last night from Louisa Hickox, a very old friend of mine, that your Major Carter is in town. He's staying at his friend Marcus Ravenhurst's house in Berkeley Square.'

'He isn't *my* Major Carter,' Verity pointed out with a touch of asperity.

'Well, dear, you know what I mean. I discovered, too, that he is paying particular attention to three young ladies. So it looks as though he's thinking of settling down. And that's no bad thing if he does come into the title, which looks more likely with every passing day.'

Verity didn't bother to respond to this at all. Instead, she asked, 'Do you happen to know if Uncle Charles is in town?'

Lady Billington detected nothing amiss in this sudden and unexpected enquiry. Verity had never made any secret of the fact that Lord Charles was her favourite male member of the Harcourt family, and she had been naughty enough to suggest on more than one occasion that it was a great pity that he had not been the eldest son, for he would have made a fine duke as he was by far the most intelligent member of the family.

'I should imagine so, dear. He rarely leaves London. His only real love is his career, as you very well know.' She shrugged one plump shoulder. 'It's probably just as well he never married, I suppose.'

'You appear to have marriage on the brain this morning. There are worse fates than remaining unattached, Aunt Clara,' Verity remarked, rising from the table. 'I think I shall pay him an impromptu visit. I haven't set eyes on him in a twelvemonth.'

'Very well, dear,' Lady Billington responded, her unruffled complacency having by this time returned, 'but do not be too long. Remember we are to visit the dressmaker later this morning.'

'I shall be back in good time,' Verity assured her. 'And what is more,' she added, casting her eyes in the direction of the comfortable winged chair in the corner of the room in which her aunt's pampered pet lay contentedly dozing, 'I shall be kind to Horace and take him with me. The only exercise that poor creature ever gets is jumping in and out of your carriage. The walk will do him good.'

Lady Billington regarded her beloved pet in some concern, but a short while later, as she watched Verity leave the house with her maid, and with Horace tripping quite contentedly alongside, her dreadful fear that her precious Pekinese might betray displeasure at the forced excursion by nipping at a neatly turned ankle and end its days by being thrown into the murky grey waters of the Thames was dispelled.

Lord Charles Harcourt's residence was only a twenty-minute walk from his sister's fashionable town house in Curzon Street. Even Horace was not in the least fatigued as he clambered up the stone steps. On his best behaviour, he sat and waited patiently until the door was opened by a very morose-looking individual who, after casting an expert eye over the caller's fashionable pale blue walking dress and matching pelisse, announced that his master was not receiving that morning.

'Oh, is he not?' Verity responded lightly, with a steely look in her eyes which both her aunt and uncle would have recognised instantly but which the butler, never having seen her before, was unable to interpret until a moment later, when she all but thrust him aside as she marched resolutely into the hall. 'I am not here to pay a social call. You may tell my uncle that I need to see him on a most urgent matter which will take a few minutes only of his time.'

There was no mistaking the determination in the pleasant voice. There was no doubt, either, that the young person was quality born; it showed in every line of her slender form. But it was the magic word 'uncle' which finally persuaded the butler to disregard his master's direct orders and disturb him.

'His lordship has someone with him at present, miss. But if you would care to step in here,' he invited, opening a door on the left of the hall, 'I shall inform him you are here.'

Surprisingly, Verity was forced to wait in the small salon overlooking the street for no more than a minute or so before the butler returned to say that his lordship would receive her now. Leaving Horace in Meg's care, she followed the high-ranking servant across the hall and into the well-stocked library where her uncle was seated behind a huge mahogany desk.

He rose at once and came towards her to place an avuncular peck on her cheek. 'My dear, you get prettier each time I see you. Can I offer you some refreshments?'

'No, thank you, Uncle Charles. I know you're extremely busy, so I shan't take up too much of your time.' She frowned suddenly, casting a glance round the large, book-lined room. 'I thought you had someone with you?'

'No, no, my dear. He—er—left some time ago. And I'm never too busy to see my favourite niece.' Nodding dismissal to his butler, Lord Charles showed Verity to the chair placed beside the desk before resuming his own seat. 'So, Clara did manage to get you to town, did she? I never thought I'd live to see you enjoying a Season.'

'She certainly did manage to persuade me, but whether I enjoy the experience remains to be seen,' she responded drily. 'We travelled from Aunt Clara's home in Kent yesterday. And that is why I have come to talk to you, Uncle Charles.'

Verity subjected him to a rather thoughtful stare. His career in politics had spanned many years, but she had never quite understood the precise nature of the work he undertook for the government—although she did know that he had travelled many times to Portugal and Spain during the Peninsular Campaign, and knew too that he was well acquainted with the Duke of Wellington.

'One of the traces broke on Aunt Clara's travelling carriage,' she explained, 'and as I flatly refused to travel with my aunt's pets I took a seat on the mail.' She then went on to divulge in detail what had taken place in the small room at that wayside inn, and experienced a twinge of annoyance when, after learning all, he just sat there regarding her quite blandly, as though she had furnished him with nothing of more importance that the latest fashion in bonnets.

'Well?' she prompted, a touch of asperity creeping into her voice, when he still remained silent.

'Yes—er—very interesting, my dear, but I don't think we need concern ourselves unduly.'

'You don't think. . .?' Verity regarded him in open-mouthed astonishment, unable to believe that the uncle she had always regarded so highly could say anything so crassly stupid. 'Have you listened to a single word I've said, Uncle Charles?'

'Of course I have. Now, calm down, child,' he said soothingly, after noting the angry flash in her violet-blue eyes. 'I shall ensure that what you've told me is passed on to the—er—necessary quarter.' He waved his hand in a dismissive gesture. 'But we hear accounts of suspected spies all the time, and most turn out to be complete nonsense. So the best thing you can do is not to worry that pretty head of yours about it any more and forget that it ever happened.'

'I see.' Knowing that it would be a complete waste of breath to discuss the matter further, Verity rose to her feet. 'I'm sorry I took up so much of your valuable time, Uncle Charles.'

The thread of sarcasm woven into her voice did not go unnoticed, but he thought it wisest to ignore it. 'Not at all, my dear. I'm always pleased to see you. Tell your aunt that I'll call on her soon, and if you can keep an evening free during your stay in town, perhaps you'll permit your old uncle Charles to take you to the theatre?'

Smiling fondly, he escorted her to the front door, but the instant he returned to his library the smile was replaced by a troubled frown. He went across to the window and followed his niece's progress along the street until she disappeared from view.

'I take it you heard all that?'

The door leading to the small ante-room was thrown wide and a tall gentleman strolled into the library. 'Yes, I heard,' he replied, seating himself in the chair Verity had just vacated. 'Very interesting, and very valuable information. It's a pity your niece didn't get a clear view of the messenger. And it's a pity that I didn't notice anyone leave, either. But then—' he shrugged his broad shoulders '—I wasn't expecting any contact to be made with our little Frenchman at that unscheduled stop.'

'It was fortuitous that Verity overheard that conversation. But I could wish she had not.' Lord Charles turned away from the window and fixed his gaze on the gentleman sprawled at his ease in the chair. 'You omitted to inform me that you had picked her up, m'boy.'

A rather rueful smile curled the younger man's attractive mouth. 'I was given strict instructions not to pick anyone up who wasn't on the waybill, but I could hardly leave her there, now, could I? I had forgotten that you two were related.' He shook his head in disbelief. 'I must say she has changed. I hardly recognised her.'

Lord Charles, his heavy frown still very much in evidence, resumed his seat at the desk. 'My memory has been equally at fault. I'd forgotten that Lucius Redmond's house in Yorkshire is quite close to your own.'

'Less than three miles.'

'And I suppose you knew her well at one time?'

'Very.'

'Is there any possibility that she recognised you?'

'No, I'm positive she didn't. The last time we met she was little more than a child.'

'Mmm.' Lord Charles's worried frown grew more

pronounced. 'But she's a child no longer. She can be a
headstrong little filly at times,' he muttered, much to his
visitor's evident amusement. 'There's no saying what
she may do now. . . And I didn't handle that little interview with her at all well.'

Lord Charles had good reason to be concerned. Although
betraying no outward signs as she made her way back
to Curzon Street, nor later that morning when she accompanied her aunt to the dressmaker's, Verity was both hurt
and angry over her uncle's seeming indifference to her
disclosures. She was not even certain in her own mind
that he would pass on the information given to him, let
alone ensure that something positive was done to catch
that spy and his villainous, traitorous associates. After
all, hadn't her uncle pooh-poohed it as nothing important,
a mere bagatelle? So what possible reliance could she
place on him?

None whatsoever, she decided, glancing with scant
enthusiasm at the lengths of lovely materials brought
from the store-room for her inspection. Therefore it was
up to her to convince him that she was not some feather-
brained female who was merely overreacting. . . But
how? What could she possibly do?

She was still pondering over this rather ticklish problem, while waiting for Lady Billington to make up her
mind on whether to have one of her new gowns made
up in pearl-grey or puce, when she looked up to discover
she was being regarded rather thoughtfully by a young
lady, modishly attired in a pale green carriage dress,
seated by the window. The face beneath the dashing
bonnet was quite lovely, and there was more than just a
hint of amusement in the grey-green eyes which remained

staring fixedly, and rather rudely, Verity considered, in her direction. She was about to bestow a look of hauteur on the ill-mannered person when the young lady unexpectedly rose from the chair and moved gracefully towards her.

'Forgive me for staring so,' she said, in a voice every bit as attractive as her smile, 'but am I right in thinking that you are Miss Harcourt. . . Miss Verity Harcourt, who used to attend Miss Tinsdale's seminary in Bath?'

'Yes, I am.' Rising to her feet, Verity subjected the young woman's face to a rather piercing scrutiny. 'Elizabeth?' Both expression and voice betrayed uncertainty. 'Elizabeth Beresford?'

At the nod of confirmation Verity gave an unmaidenly shriek and threw her arms round the young woman, much to the staunch disapproval of a rather forbidding-looking matron who had just entered the premises. 'I would never have recognised you,' she said with brutal frankness. 'You're so thin!'

Far from offended, Elizabeth gurgled with laughter. 'And you haven't changed a bit. You still say precisely what you think. That was one of the many things I admired in you.'

Verity held her friend at arm's length, still somewhat bemused. Her plump, shy and rather plain schoolfriend had blossomed into such a lovely young woman. It was incredible!

'Oh, it's so good to see you again after all these years. It was such a pity we lost touch when you left the seminary, although I did write to you.' Verity noted her friend's slight frown at this snippet of information, but as Lady Billington was approaching, she refrained from enquiring into the reason behind the slightly puzzled look.

It took Lady Billington a minute only to realise that the two girls were overjoyed to see each other again after all this time, and to come to the conclusion that her niece's friend was a sensible and well-mannered young lady. She raised no objection, therefore, when Miss Beresford suggested that, as it was such a lovely day, she and Verity would enjoy a drive round Hyde Park, and promised to restore her safely to Curzon Street later.

Verity sat herself beside Elizabeth in her friend's open carriage and for a while they reminisced about their schooldays, but then Verity changed the subject by asking her friend what she had been doing with herself since leaving the seminary.

'I well expected you to be married by now. Weren't you promised almost from birth to the son of a baronet? Quite a Gothic notion, I've always thought, but you seemed quite happy with——.' Verity caught herself up abruptly when she noticed her friend's expression change suddenly, the smile vanishing and an almost closed-up look taking possession of her features. 'Oh, Elizabeth, I am sorry! Have I said something I ought not?'

'No, no. Not at all!' Elizabeth responded, but the smile that accompanied the assurance was all too obviously false. 'Yes, Richard and I were in a way promised to each other. Our respective fathers were great friends and had always dreamed of uniting the two families by marriage. Richard, I'm certain, would have fulfilled his father's dearest wish. . . Unfortunately I felt myself unable to comply. We would not have suited.'

Elizabeth was looking directly at her, but Verity had the feeling that her friend was not seeing her but images from the past.

'You may recall my father died during my final year

at the seminary. When I refused point-blank to become betrothed to Richard the relationship between my mother and myself, which honesty prompts me to admit had never been good, deteriorated to such an extent that I felt unable to remain under the same roof as her. I ran away to my maternal grandmother in Bristol.' This time the smile was full of gentle warmth. 'Best thing I ever did! I've never looked back.'

Verity regarded her friend in a mixture of admiration and astonishment. The shy and highly sensitive, rather plump and plain girl she had known years ago had changed out of all recognition, and seemingly not only in looks.

'And do you still reside with your grandmother?' she found herself asking.

'Oh, yes. We are in London until the end of next week. Then we're off to join the throng in Brussels. My grandmother isn't well, Verity. I cannot allow her to make the journey alone and she is determined to go. She has a godson in the army and feels it her duty now that both his parents are dead to be near in case. . .' She shook her head. 'I had foolishly believed that Napoleon's exile would bring an end to all this nonsense.'

'Sadly it has not proved to be the case. And how many more must give their lives before it is finally over? And how many more could be saved if. . .?' Verity's words faded and she looked at her friend closely for a moment, hesitating, then related all she had overheard at the inn and the far from satisfactory conversation she had had with her uncle earlier that day.

Elizabeth said nothing, her expression not unlike that of Lord Charles Harcourt a couple of hours ago. Then, still without uttering a word in response, she leaned forward in her seat, gave the coachman a tap on the shoulder with her parasol and requested him to pull over as she felt the need to stretch her legs.

'So, what are you proposing to do about it now?' she asked, once they had walked several yards away from the carriage across the grass, and Verity almost sighed with relief.

'Thank heavens! I was beginning to think no one would believe me.'

'I recall your being a headstrong creature, Verity,' Elizabeth remarked candidly, her lips curling into a most attractively winning smile, 'and I doubt you've changed that much. But you were never a liar, nor even remotely fanciful. Of course I believe you! It's a thousand pities your uncle didn't, but all is not lost. Evidently your uncle is a cautious man and requires more proof of a spy network being in operation before he is prepared to act. Therefore, you must provide him with the proof.'

'Yes, but how? Short of going to this Little Frampington myself, I don't see what else I can do.' Verity caught the quizzical gleam in her friend's eyes and stopped dead in her tracks. 'Yes, I could go, couldn't I!' She fell silent for a moment, her mind working rapidly. 'If only I could manage to leave the house without arousing my aunt's suspicions. She might appear to be feather-brained, but, believe me, she's far from it.'

'And there I can be of some help to you,' Elizabeth astounded her by saying. 'It so happens that my grandmother intends holding a dinner-party on Friday evening. If it were not for that fact I wouldn't hesitate to accompany you, believe me.' There was almost a wistful note in her soft, pleasant voice. 'But the occasion will work to our advantage. What could be more natural than for me to send an invitation to you? Your aunt will suspect nothing. She saw how pleased we were to see each other. I'll send the carriage to collect you early on Friday evening. Then you can change at my grandmother's house and be on your way.'

'Change?' Verity echoed, not just a little bemused. This was all going a little too fast for her.

'You cannot possibly travel all the way to Frampington and enter this inn dressed in evening garb. I rather fancy you'd stand out a trifle. Besides which, it would be highly improper for a young lady to go careering about the country on her own. Therefore you must become a youth! Don't worry,' Elizabeth went on after receiving a rather startled look, 'I'll get clothes for you and hire a horse.'

Verity regarded her old schoolfriend with the utmost respect. 'You're a marvel, Elizabeth! I should never have thought of that. Going dressed as a boy in shabby, worn clothes. . . Yes, the perfect solution!'

'You forget I've had experience at this sort of thing. How do you think I managed to succeed in running away from my mother's house six years ago? Although, I must confess, I did have Aggie with me.'

'Aggie?' Verity echoed.

'Yes, she was our old nursemaid. She's now my personal maid. She's a dreadful scold, but a dear, and she'll do anything I ask of her. I'll get her to wait at the corner of the street for you on Friday evening. Then she can take you round to the rear of the house and up the back stairs. That way you'll not be seen by any of the other servants. Once you've changed, she will show you out to the mews where I'll arrange for the horse to be ready, saddled and awaiting you. And Aggie will watch out for you again on your return.'

'Lord, Elizabeth! You've left me with absolutely nothing to do.'

'Nothing except put your life in peril, Verity,' she countered, looked deeply troubled now. 'Oh, how I wish I could go with you!'

Verity gave her friend's arm a reassuring squeeze. 'It doesn't need two of us, and I rather think it would be better if I go on my own. Now all I need to do is find out exactly where this Little Frampington is situated. I just hope it's within easy riding distance of London, otherwise we're foiled from the start.'

'We've maps back at the house. Return with me now and we can discuss everything in detail.' Elizabeth's expression remained grave. 'Meeting up with you again after all these years has been wonderful. I just hope that I don't come to regret the encounter. It doesn't need me to warn you that these people must be dangerous, Verity. For heaven's sake, take care!'

Chapter Four

According to Elizabeth's map, the village where Verity had to lie in wait for the spy and his accomplices appeared to be no more than an hour's ride from London. Friday evening arrived and everything went according to plan. It was an added bonus that the evening was dry and far from cold. Even the hired mount, thankfully, turned out to be a sturdy, reliable beast, sound in both wind and limb. Verity felt not in the least self-conscious in her boy's raiment, but it did take her some little time to accustom herself to riding astride again after years of being forced to sit her mount like a lady. None the less, she arrived at the turn-off to Little Frampington in good time, and, after wending her way down a series of narrow, high-hedged lanes, she finally reached her destination.

Drawing her mount to a halt in the middle of the narrow street, Verity looked about her in dismay, experiencing for the first time some slight doubts as to the wisdom of her actions. The place was nothing more than a hamlet. There wasn't even a church, and the dozen or so dwellings all looked to be in need of some urgent repairs. The inn, if one could call it so, was the most ramshackle building of the lot. There were tiles missing from its roof, there wasn't a window that didn't boast at least one broken pane of glass and the door had a hole in the bottom large enough for a cat to get through, let alone a rat! No law-abiding citizen with a modicum of intelligence would ever seek succour within its walls, for it was undoubtedly a thieves' den, a meeting place for every kind of rogue for miles around.

She hadn't formulated any plan of action. If she could manage to get close enough to overhear some snippets of the conversation which passed between the spy and his associates it would be a bonus, but even she balked at the idea of entering that place. No, she had to be sensible, as Elizabeth had urged her to be on more than one occasion during the past days. The best she could hope for now was to lie in wait and watch to see who turned up for the meeting, and then give an accurate description of all the men involved to her Uncle Charles.

Dismounting, she led her mount into the stable which, though dilapidated, was certainly in a better state of repair than the tavern, and was surprised to discover a pair of perfectly matched greys still harnessed to a very smart racing curricle. One of the fine animals whinnied at her approach, and as she ran a hand down his sleek neck she noticed a black diamond-shaped blemish in the skin beneath its silken mane.

''Ere, what you be doing?' a rough voice demanded, and Verity, her heart almost missing a beat, swung round to see a coarse-looking man seated on a small stool down at the far end of the stable. Narrow-eyed, he looked her over with evident suspicion while he continued to whittle away at the piece of wood in his hand with an evil-looking knife.

'Nothing,' she responded in a rough little voice, only just remembering in time that she was supposed to be a youth.

'Well, gets yerself away from them there 'osses! I'm paid to look after they.' Verity didn't need telling twice, and the man continued his steely-eyed piercing scrutiny as she took a step away. 'What you be doing 'ere? You ain't from around these parts.'

'No, I'm not. I'm—er—supposed to be meeting someone here.' Verity's mind was working rapidly. He was evidently suspicious, but curious too, and she just might be able to turn this to her advantage. By keeping him talking she had an excuse to remain in the stable, where she had a clear view of the front entrance and would see anyone entering the inn.

Who yer s'posed to be meeting?'

'My uncle.'

'Yer uncle, eh? Who be that, then—Old Pike the Poacher?' He guffawed at his pathetic whimsy. 'What be yer uncle's name, lad?'

'Septimus Watts,' she responded, hoping Lady Billington's strait-laced butler wouldn't object to her making free with his name.

'Never 'eard of 'im.'

'Maybe not,' Verity returned, determined to brazen it out, 'but he still asked me to meet him here, outside the inn at Little Frampington.'

He guffawed again, only louder this time. 'Best be on yer way then, yer brainless cur. Little Frampington be a mile or so further on down the road.'

'Wh-what?' It was Verity's turn to stare this time. 'But this is Little Frampington, surely? I saw the signpost back along the road.'

'No, it ain't! This be Frampington. And I should know...lived in this Godforsaken 'ole most all m'life. The place you be wanting be further down the road. So best be on yer way.'

Verity had no reason to doubt him. What could he possibly gain by lying to her, after all? Without a word of farewell, which she doubted would have been appreciated anyway, she led her mount out of the stable while cursing herself silently under her breath. She ought to have studied Elizabeth's map more closely! She could have sworn, though, that there hadn't been two Frampingtons shown. Evidently this place was considered too insignificant to warrant a mention!

Not wasting a precious moment, Verity urged her mount out of the yard and into the narrow street. Although she had left London early, allowing for the possibility that she might just take a wrong turning, she knew that it must be close on eight o'clock by now, and she dug her heels hard into the gelding's flanks, but to little effect. He had proved himself to be steady and reliable, but he certainly hadn't been bred for speed, and the church clock had just finished chiming the hour as she arrived at the village of Little Frampington, which belied its name by being many times larger than its namesake back along the road.

Verity located the inn, which was situated directly opposite the church, without any difficulty. Dismounting, she led her mount into the stable and almost sighed with relief when she saw just one large bay champing away contentedly on a pile of hay. Unless that spy and his associates had made the journey on foot they had not arrived yet. She was in time!

She experienced no qualms whatsoever over entering

this well-maintained building, with its whitewashed cob walls and undulating, neatly thatched roof. The interior, she discovered as she entered the tap, was further proof that mine host was both conscientious and hard-working. There was a welcoming fire in the large inglenook fireplace, the grey-stone floor had certainly seen a brush that day, and there wasn't a table—except those occupied by the customers—which had so much as a single smear to mar its highly polished surface.

Making her way over to the counter, behind which a young woman in a pristine white apron stood serving a customer, Verity cast her eyes over the other patrons, most of whom were seated at the various tables. All bore the appearance of working men, refreshing themselves after a hard day's toil. Could one of them possibly be the man who had arranged to meet that spy? She cast a further surreptitious glance over them. They appeared to be farmers or labourers, their leathery, weather-beaten faces proof enough that they were accustomed to working out of doors. It was hard to imagine that any one of them could be the spy's accomplice, unless of course he was in disguise. And one of them certainly wasn't a local, she reminded herself, recalling the large, handsome bay in the stable.

'What can I get for you, young sir?'

Verity very nearly betrayed her true sex by stupidly asking for a glass of ratafia, but managed to check herself just in time and request a tankard of ale. Quickly turning her grimace into a smile as she took her first sip, she leaned against the counter, hoping she resembled a swaggering youth.

'You keep a fine inn,' she remarked.

'Why, thank you, sir! My ma and pa do like the place looking clean and tidy.'

So, she was the daughter of the house, Verity mused. That might prove useful. 'Yes, it's certainly better kept than a good many posting houses I've been in. Do you have rooms for hire here, or do you cater only for local trade?'

'Oh, we do have rooms, sir, but it's not often they're used. Not being on one of the main posting roads, we don't get too many travellers coming this way. Although,' she went on, casting her rather attractive soft brown eyes about the room, 'we did have a gentleman in earlier requesting a room. Can't see him about now. Must have finished his dinner and gone back upstairs.'

Verity's eyes narrowed speculatively as she risked a further sip of the home-brewed. How very interesting. Was he merely an innocent traveller or the traitorous wretch who had arranged to meet the spy?

'My aunt travels about the country quite a bit,' she informed the landlord's daughter in a conversational tone. 'She dislikes the noisy posting houses and much prefers to put up at quiet inns like this one. Do you happen to have a private parlour? I'm afraid she would never consider dining in the tap.'

'Yes, sir. It's upstairs. I'd willingly show it you, only it's been hired for the evening and the gentlemen will be here soon. They frequently hire the parlour for an evening.'

The ale was, surprisingly, becoming more palatable with each mouthful, Verity decided, sampling the home-brewed yet again as she watched the daughter of the house move away to serve another customer. So, these so-called gentlemen had met here before, had they? The innkeeper's daughter had been most informative, and Verity would not hesitate to pass on what she had learned to Lord Charles in the morning. A watch must be put on this place, but it might be some time before the spy met his accomplices again. . .and what of tonight's meeting?

Verity had well and truly got the bit between her teeth. Her Uncle Charles hadn't taken her seriously, but she was determined that he would do so after this night's escapade. Resolve added an extra sparkle to her eyes. If she remained where she was she couldn't fail to see who went upstairs to the private parlour, but now she wanted to discover more. Those men were meeting here for some purpose, possibly to make plans or maybe to exchange vital information, but no matter the reason Verity wanted to know exactly what passed between them, and the only way to achieve her objective was to hide in that upstairs parlour.

She looked across at the door, which stood slightly ajar and which in all probability led to the upper floor. After only a moment's indecision, she made her way as surreptitiously as possible towards it. One swift glance about the room was sufficient to assure her that no one was looking in her direction, and she slipped through the opening to find herself in a small lobby with the stairs rising directly ahead.

Mounting them swiftly and silently, Verity stepped onto a narrow, ill-lit landing, the only light coming from a small window at the far end. There were several doors on both left and right at intervals along the passageway. Reaching the first, she tentatively turned the knob and, poking her head into the room, discovered it to be a small and tidy bedchamber. The second led to yet another bedchamber, but the third gave access to the room she

had been seeking. The curtains had been drawn across
the window and candles burning brightly in their sconces
bathed the small parlour in a warm, welcoming glow.
There were glasses and a bottle set on the table in the
centre of the room in readiness for the hirers, but nothing,
not even a screen, behind which she could hide.

Disappointed, but far from disheartened, Verity closed
the parlour door quietly and was pondering on what she
could do when she noticed a door on the opposite side
and a little further along the passageway was slightly ajar.
Her eyes narrowed speculatively. Might it be possible to
wait in there, keeping watch? It would offer a clear view
of anyone entering the parlour. Then, when the spy and
his associates had arrived, she could step across the passageway, place her ear to the door and with any luck
overhear what was being said.   The only slight problem
that she could envisage was if the room happened to be
the bedchamber of the landlord and his wife, or their
daughter, but even if this did turn out to be the case she
doubted that any one of them would retire for the night
until the last of the customers had departed. Yes, she
would risk it!

Pushing the door open, she took a hesitant step into
the room. The curtains had been drawn, effectively blocking out the rapidly fading late-evening light, but she could
make out the bed at the far end and, thankfully, it wasn't
occupied. She breathed a sigh of relief, and had just
taken a further tentative step forward when she detected
a sudden movement.

Before she knew what was happening her waist had
been encircled by something strongly resembling an iron
band and a large hand had been clapped over her mouth,
effectively preventing the terrified squeal which rose in

her throat from escaping. Dear God. . .! The guest! She'd completely forgotten about him.

The pulsating throb in her temples beat a vicious tattoo in her ears as her captor kicked the door shut. The heat from his powerful body penetrated her boy's raiment as she struggled wildly in a valiant attempt to break free, but her efforts were in vain. The muscular arm encircling her was immovable, and the hand over her mouth held her head firmly against a stone-hard chest. Then, without warning, he removed his arm from about her waist and tore the battered, misshapen hat from her head, allowing her silky black locks freedom to cascade about her shoulders.

'I thought as much,' a vaguely familiar, accented voice growled in her ear, but Verity was in no mood to work out the possible identity of her captor.

Half out of her mind with fear at what he might do next, she felt the fingers over her mouth slacken a little and didn't hesitate to take advantage. In one slight, yet swift movement she jerked her head and sank her small white teeth hard into the fleshy part of his hand just below the thumb. A smothered oath followed as Verity made a heroic dive for the doorknob, but a moment later that well-muscled limb had her imprisoned once more and she was lifted quite off her feet.

Carrying her effortlessly under one arm, as though she weighed no more than a sack of grain, her captor strode purposefully across to the bed, where he sat himself, and before Verity could do much else other than utter a gasp in protest she found herself face down over a pair of muscular thighs. Her squeals of dissent quickly turned into cries of pain as he administered half a dozen or so smarting and humiliating slaps to the seat of her breeches with the flat of his hand, before tipping her quite callously off his knee so that she landed on the floor with a further painful thud.

No one, not even her father, had ever laid a hand on her before, and a combination of anger and resentment, not to mention bruised pride, welled up inside.

Fear was suddenly a thing of the past as Verity swept the tangled mat of hair from her face and peered up at the brutish individual who had dared to treat her in such a fashion. Through the haze of tears she saw a tricorn hat pulled low over eyes, a face hidden by a muffler, and a powerful body swathed in a dark grey cloak. There could be no mistaking who it was.

'You!' she managed in a choked whisper, scarcely believing the evidence of her own eyes.

'Aye, lass. And tha can thank thy lucky stars it is. Had it been our little Frenchman or one of 'is friends, tha wouldn't be snivelling over just a walloped backside,' the Coachman told her with brutal frankness. 'And don't wipe thy nose on thy sleeve!'

'I haven't got a handkerchief,' she muttered broodingly, and was promptly offered his own, which she accepted with as much grace as she could muster. Then, after using it thoroughly, blowing her small straight nose and wiping her eyes, she offered it back.

He regarded the crumpled ball with distaste. 'Nay. Best tha keeps it. It'll be a memento, like, a reminder not to do anything so damnably foolish again.' Folding his arms across his chest, he cast his eyes over her attire. 'Tha don't imagine, surely, those clothes ud fool anyone? Tha's far too pretty t' be a lad.'

Ignoring the compliment, she flashed him a resentful look from beneath moist lashes. 'Well, and what was I

supposed to do? I couldn't come here dressed in petticoats, now, could I?'

'Tha shouldn't be 'ere at all!'

'And I certainly wouldn't be if I had thought my uncle
intended acting on the information I'd given him!' she
countered, her spirit returning. She scrambled to her feet
and moved several paces away. 'And what are you doing
here?' She looked at him consideringly, curiosity for the
moment overriding bitter resentment. 'Were you tooling
that mail-coach to keep an eye on that Swiss gentleman?'

'Aye. Only 'e ain't Swiss, lass.' E's French, one of
Napoleon's top agents.'

Again she cast him a rather thoughtful look. 'Do you
work for Lord Charles?'

'It'd be more accurate t'say I'm working wi' 'im at
the moment. And it does 'elp our cause if t'information
passed on to us is accurate. This meeting is due t' take
place at nine o'clock, not eight, as you said. T'landlady
kindly volunteered that snippet not long after I'd arrived.'

Verity frowned. She could have sworn the time
arranged was eight o'clock. 'Well, I've learned something, too,' she told him, determined to prove that her
presence here had not been a complete waste of time.
'They've met at this place before, so it might be worthwhile keeping a watch on this inn.' Bending, she retrieved
her hat, which he had thrown on the floor. 'But, as you're
here, there's no need for me to remain. I'd better be
getting back to London.'

'Oh, no tha doesn't, lass!' he growled, arresting her
progress to the door. 'Tha's staying right, 'ere wi' me.
I'll escort thee back t'town when us friends 'ave left.
So—,' he tapped the portion of bed beside him '—come

and sit thissen down and mek thissen comfortable. We might be in for a long wait.'

'Sit?' The malevolent look she cast him would have withered a lesser mortal. 'You've made sure I'll not be able to do that with any degree of comfort for some considerable time!'

'N' more than tha deserved,' was his indifferent response to her hurts. 'Tha were always a 'eadstrong, spoilt filly, wanting thy way in everything. And getting it most o' the time, more's the pity. Redmond ought to 'ave schooled you years ago, then it'd 'ave saved me the trouble.' His eyes narrowed as he looked her up and down. 'And I doubt I've finished yet, tha troublesome chit!'

Verity bit back the angry rejoinder which rose in her throat as yet another thought struck her. She looked across at him keenly, but there was insufficient light to enable her to see him clearly. Besides which, the muffler hid too much of his face for her to recognise him.

'You know my Uncle Lucius, don't you? And we've met before. . . Who are you?'

'Aye, I knows 'im, reet enough. And I've seen thee about in Yorkshire. But as t'who I be. . .'Tis best tha don't know for the time being, lass, I'm merely. . .the Coachman.'

Verity was far from satisfied with that, but before she was able to probe further there was a noise outside on the landing, followed by the sounds of jovial voices. She cast a questioning glance at the Coachman, who placed a warning finger to his lips as he rose from the bed.

For a tall, powerfully built man he was remarkably light on his feet, hardly making a sound as he moved with lightning speed across the room. He waited a moment or

two, listening intently, before opening the door a fraction
and placing one eye to the crack. Verity could hear the
voices clearly too, but surprisingly not one bore a trace
of a foreign accent. Then the parlour door closed and the
Coachman looked back at her with what could only be
described as a rather suspicious glint in his eyes.

'If tha's dragged me all t' way out 'ere on some fool's
errand, lass, so elp me, I'll—'

'Why? What is it? What's wrong,' she interrupted.
'Wasn't the Frenchman with them?'

'No, 'e weren't. I'm goin' in there. And just in case
tha think t' give me the slip,' he added, removing the
key, 'I'm goin' t'take the precaution o' locking you in.'
Then, without giving her the opportunity to protest, he
placed himself on the other side of the door, and before
she could move the key turned in the lock.

Her eyes were deep blue pools of seething resentment.
Confound the odious brute! He had no right to imprison
her! Verity was almost beside herself with rage. She took
a hasty step towards the door, intending to pound her
fists against the solid wood and shout at the top of her
voice, but then she checked herself as sense prevailed.
By doing so she might alert the men in the room opposite,
put them on their guard. Not only that, she wouldn't put
it past the Coachman to return and repeat the brutish
treatment he had meted out earlier if she caused a stir.

Still highly resentful, she swung round, about to take
his rather insensitive advice and sit on the bed, when
the floral-patterned curtains at the window caught her
attention. The door might be locked. . .but what about
the window?

Throwing back the drapes, she saw that the window
was small, but certainly large enough for her to climb

out. It was quite dark now, but she had no difficulty in seeing, as the window blessedly opened with ease, a single-story construction with a sloping roof directly below. Remaining only for the time it took to securely confine her long hair back in the misshapen hat, she clambered onto the sill and out into the cool night air. Then, tiptoeing lightly over the tiles, she perched herself on the edge of the roof and, with the aid of a large and conveniently placed wooden barrel, had no difficulty in reaching the ground.

She hadn't taken more than a step or two towards the stables when a door behind her opened and she swung round, her breath leaving her in a sigh of relief when she saw the landlord's daughter, wrapped in a serviceable cloak, step outside.

'Oh, it's you, young sir! I thought you'd left long since.' She cast Verity one of her rather sweet, friendly smiles. 'I'm just off up the road,' she explained, falling into step beside the very handsome 'youth', 'to take this basket of food to an old lady.'

'And I'm ready to leave now,' Verity responded, remembering to keep her voice low. 'I've—er—just been taking a stroll round this village of yours. I'm certain my aunt would be quite happy to stay overnight here.'

'It's a nice quiet place, sir. I'm sorry I weren't able to show you the parlour, but old Colonel Hanbury is a funny old stick. Wouldn't like it none if he discovered someone in there when he'd paid for its hire.'

'Colonel Hanbury?' Verity echoed, and the girl gurgled with laughter.

'It's supposed to be a secret, but everyone round these parts knows,' she confided in a conspiratorial whisper. 'Everyone except their wives, that is. The colonel, the vicar and the old doctor meet here twice a month. Their wives disapprove of gaming, you see. So for a quiet life they comes here.'

Oh, God! Verity groaned inwardly. When the Coachman discovered who they were, and she didn't doubt for a moment that he would, he'd be absolutely furious with her, truly believing she had brought him out here on some wild-goose chase. . . And how could she prove otherwise? The sooner she departed the better!

After a hurriedly spoken farewell to the landlord's daughter. Verity collected her mount from the stable, wincing slightly as she got into the saddle.

The ride.back to London was both uncomfortable and nerve-racking. Each time she detected the sound of hoof-beats she would take a quick glance over her shoulder, expecting to see the Coachman in hot pursuit, his cloak billowing, his brow as darkly threatening as a thunder-cloud, and it was only when she had at last reached the capital, where she was able to mingle with the carriages and other riders in the surprisingly busy night streets, that she began to relax a little.

She arrived at the house Elizabeth's grandmother had hired feeling thoroughly miserable and dejected. All the carefully made plans had been for nothing. The visit to Little Frampington had been a complete and utter waste of time and effort. But what had gone wrong?

Verity just couldn't understand it at all, and shook her head in complete bewilderment. So, she might have got the time of the meeting wrong, but certainly not the place, she felt certain of that. Little Frampington, that Frenchman had said. . . No, he hadn't, she amended silently, her brows drawing together in deep thought. His exact words had been 'zee leetle leetle Frampington.'

Oh, no! Closing her eyes, Verity cursed herself for a fool. Frampington was smaller than its near neighbour, and that was what the Frenchman had meant. Of all the stupid Gallic jokes! The meeting had taken place at that rundown old tavern! She could have screamed in vexation. All that time and effort! And what had she got to show for it. . .? Nothing except a bruised rear!

Chapter Five

'**Y**ou must stop brooding over it, Verity, and blaming yourself. What more could you possibly have done, for heaven's sake!'

It was almost a week since she had made that futile trip to Little Frampington, and her complete lack of success had continued to weigh heavily on her mind. She had well expected a visit from an irate Lord Charles Harcourt, blaming her entirely for wasting his associate's time, but she had not set eyes on him, nor had she received any communication, written or otherwise, during the intervening days. Which was most strange, in the circumstances. Surely the Coachman wouldn't have hesitated in reporting back to him, assuring him that the meeting which had taken place at that inn had been merely a gathering of three law-abiding local inhabitants out enjoying nothing more sinister than a night's gaming?

Verity managed a wan smile, but it was an effort. 'Yes, of course you're right, Elizabeth. There was nothing more I could have done. I've been pretty poor company these past days, I know. And here you are leaving tomorrow for Brussels.' She gave her friend's arm an affectionate squeeze. 'When shall we see each other again, I wonder?'

'Not for several months, I'm afraid. But this time, Verity, I'm determined we shan't lose touch.'

'I did receive one letter from you whilst I was still at the seminary, Elizabeth, and I did write to you several times during my final year there, but never received anything further,' Verity assured her, remembering the strange look on her friend's face when she had mentioned this before. This time Elizabeth was a little more forthcoming.

'After leaving the seminary, I didn't remain very long at my mother's house. She never forwarded one of your letters on to me. I foolishly assumed that you had forgotten your old schoolfriend, but I shan't make that mistake again,' Elizabeth assured her. 'My grandmother's courier has made all the arrangements on our behalf, and I'm not in possession of our precise direction in Brussels, but once we've arrived I shall write and let you know. And when we return you must come and stay with us in Bristol.' A wickedly provocative smile hovered about her mouth. 'If you're not betrothed by then, that is.'

Verity pulled a face of disgust. 'No fear of that, my dear friend.'

There was more than a hint of derision in her voice, and Elizabeth looked at her closely. 'Am I right in thinking that, when we were at school together, you mentioned you were very fond of a certain someone? In fact, I believe you said you were in love.'

'Ha!' Verity scoffed, waving her hand in an impatient gesture. 'Puppy love. Thank the good Lord I've more sense now!'

Elizabeth couldn't prevent a smile at the scathing tone and, after nodding to an acquaintance who passed walking in the opposite direction, said, 'What happened, Verity? How did the man whose name I'm afraid I cannot recall now give you such a dislike of him?'

'Brin Carter. . .now Major Carter,' Verity responded after a moment's silence, staring fixedly ahead. 'He once held a place in my affections but, as I've already mentioned, I was very young. . .and rather foolish to have thought so well of him.'

'Brin. . .? What an unusual name!'

'He was named after his maternal grandfather. Well, it was his grandfather's surname, at any rate. It's an abbreviation. It's Brinley, really.'

'What happened?' Elizabeth prompted gently.

'Oh, nothing very much. I believed myself in love with him, but my affections were not reciprocated. Brin was besotted with the daughter of the local squire. Angela Kingsley was, and still is for that matter, an ethereal creature with the face of an angel, a figure many a female would sell her soul to possess and the heart of a moneylender. Brin would never hear a word said against her. When I tried to tell him that his beloved Angela was not quite all that she seemed, he told me in no uncertain terms that I was nothing more than a spoilt and spiteful little cat who ought to be taught some manners.'

Her sudden shout of laughter was a rather bitter, hollow sound. 'To cut a long story short, while Brin was fighting for his country in the Peninsula, Angela, who had promised faithfully to await his return, upped and married that great tub of lard Sir Frederick Morland. Now, whether or not Brin himself believed that cock-and-bull story she put about that her family had forced her into the union, I've no idea, for I've neither spoken to him nor indeed set eyes on him in the past five years.'

Elizabeth was silent for a moment, staring fixedly ahead down the park's tree-lined path, then said with that uncanny insight she had possessed even as a young girl, 'I cannot help but wonder, Verity, if you are as indifferent to the Major as you claim to be. After all, you have never bestowed your affection on another.'

'No, very true,' she concurred. 'But pray do not be under the misapprehension that I've been nursing a broken heart all this time, because I tell you plainly I have not! I simply have more sense now than to bestow affection where it is neither desired nor appreciated.'

'You dismiss it lightly enough, my dear, but I suspect he hurt you very deeply.'

Verity didn't attempt to respond. They had by this time arrived at Elizabeth's carriage, which had stood under the shade of some trees whilst they had taken a turn round the park. Elizabeth made to mount the steps, but Verity arrested her by placing a hand on her arm.

'I think I'll walk back to Curzon Street with Meg. So I shall bid you goodbye here.' She gave Elizabeth a quick hug. 'Take care, my friend.'

'I shall. And let us say, rather, farewell.' Concern was mirrored in Elizabeth's grey-green eyes. 'Don't permit your recent disappointment at Little Frampington to shadow the rest of your stay in London. And, more importantly, don't let past hurts prevent you from forming a lasting attachment to some gentleman worthy of your affections, my dear.'

Verity couldn't prevent a rather rueful little smile at this. 'If I met a man whom I believed would make me happy, and I him, then I would consider marrying. But I don't expect I shall find him amongst the dashing sprigs I have met since my arrival in town. And I certainly shan't return to Yorkshire with a bruised ego if I end the Season still unattached. Be sure of that!'

As Verity watched the carriage move away and raised her hand in a final salute of farewell, she had to own that Elizabeth had given her much to ponder over. She would have been the first to admit that she didn't make friends easily, that she held only a handful of people in high esteem and that she bestowed genuine affection on very few. Was this the legacy of her once bruised and battered feelings? Surely not! She had got over Brin Carter years ago, hadn't given him more than a passing thought in a very long time. But she couldn't deny that she had tended to keep young, unattached gentlemen at a distance. Was this because she considered them for the most part nothing more than empty-headed nincompoops? Or could it possibly be that deep down she was trying to protect her young heart from being bruised and battered again?

She was still pondering over this rather disturbing possibility as she headed towards the gateway. Meg, tripping along beside her, was trying her best to draw her attention to a lady in a very fashionable bonnet, which Meg thought would suit her young mistress very well, but Verity paid little heed. Nor did she pay much attention to the very smart equipage drawing up alongside, until her name hailed in an ear-piercing, high-pitched voice broke into her rather distressing reflections and she raised her eyes to see the daughter of her Uncle Lucius's nearest neighbour.

Only it wasn't the sight of Hilary Fenner which caused Verity's heart to lurch suddenly and quite inexplicably, and caused her to blink several times, as though to dispel an image conjured up by her mind's eye, but the sight of that tall, broad-shouldered gentleman seated beside the lively auburn-haired girl in the curricle.

'I wondered if we would run across each other whilst in London, Verity,' Hilary gushed in her friendly way, but in a voice which had the unfortunate tendency to grate on one after a while. 'And just look who has kindly taken me for a jaunt in his smart turn-out! You remember Brin, don't you?'

Verity gazed into eyes which smiled down at her with a rather disturbing glint in their tawny depths. Silently, she was forced to admit that the years had been kind to Brin Carter. He was as devastatingly good-looking as he had been five years ago, perhaps a little more so now that time had added extra character to his face: tiny lines at the corners of his eyes and rather attractive deep clefts on either side of a mouth that was both well-shaped and rather sensual.

Her pulse continued to behave erratically, and she despised herself for being so idiotically feminine as to be beguiled, still, by his handsome face. She gave herself an inward shake, determined to overcome this foolish weakness which she believed she had conquered years ago, and, prompted by some imp of pure mischief and the strong urge to let him know that she was completely indifferent to him now, said, 'Er—forgive me, sir. Your face does look vaguely familiar, but I'm afraid I cannot recall just at the moment where we have met before.'

'Oh, Verity!' Miss Fenner gave a trill of laughter. 'You cannot have forgotten! You were so very fond of Arthur Brinley. This is his grandson.'

'Of course!' Verity was gratified to see by the slight narrowing of those attractive almond-shaped eyes that he was piqued. 'You must forgive me, sir, but it has been some years since we last met.'

'Indeed it has, Miss Harcourt,' he concurred in a voice as richly smooth as velvet. 'You were little more than a child. And may I add you have changed very little.'

She looked at him sharply, suspecting his last remark of being far from complimentary, but before she could formulate a barbed response Miss Fenner interposed with, 'Will you be attending Lady Morland's party tomorrow evening? Both Brin and I shall be there.'

What a merry meeting that was destined to be! Verity mused, wondering if Brin had seen his beloved Angela since her marriage to the obese baronet. She lowered her eyes in an attempt to hide the wicked amusement dancing there, and her attention was drawn to the perfectly matched greys harnessed to the curricle.

Instantly her light-heartedness vanished. She had seen this turn-out before. She felt certain of it! Taking a step towards the fine gelding nearest to her, she ran her hand down his sleek neck and had no difficulty locating that tell-tale diamond-shaped blemish beneath the mane. What in the world had Brin Carter been doing at that tumbledown old tavern last Friday evening?

She looked up again, only to discover that he was staring at her rather intently. 'I'm not perfectly certain what Lady Billington has planned for the evening, Hilary, but if Lady Morland has sent an invitation, no doubt we shall see one another again there.'

She took a hasty step back onto the grass and forced herself to meet the Major's intent gaze. 'Well, I must not detain you further. You are no doubt loath to keep these beautiful horses of yours standing too long, sir.'

'To agree would show me in a very poor light, Miss

Harcourt.' His intent look vanished as a twitching smile pulled at the corners of his attractive mouth. 'You would believe I placed the welfare of my cattle above the pleasure of conversing with you.'

'It would show sound judgement if you did, sir. One does not come across such beautiful creatures very often.'

'No, indeed one does not, Miss Harcourt,' he agreed softly, as he continued to stare down at her fixedly, but with such a depth of warmth in his eyes now that her tongue for some inexplicable reason suddenly decided to attach itself to the roof of her mouth, and she was unable to respond to his cheerful farewell before he gave the horses their office to start.

Pulling herself together with an effort, she watched the equipage mingle with the other carriages along the busy track. Then, swinging round on her heels, she marched resolutely towards the park gate, her mind so plagued by troubled thoughts that she once again took little heed of Meg's light-hearted conversation, until she received a rather urgent tug on the arm, which was impossible to ignore, and was forced to abandon her depressing reflections.

'Yes, what is it, Meg?'

'You're going the wrong way, miss.'

'No, I'm not. I'm going to pay a call on my Uncle Charles,' Verity informed her, her voice betraying clearly enough that she wasn't looking forward to the encounter with any degree of enthusiasm.

When she arrived at Lord Charles's house a short while later, his butler at least betrayed no signs of not being pleased to see her. He invited her quite cordially to step into the hall, where he left her while he informed his master of her arrival, and moments later she was asked to step into the library.

Leaving Meg to seat herself on one of the comfortable chairs in the hall, Verity entered her uncle's inner sanctum to discover him seated as usual behind the huge mahogany desk, busily writing a letter. Not even by the slight raising of one greying brow did he betray any sign of surprise at her unexpected visit, but neither, which was more ominous, did his lips curl into their usual smile of greeting before he asked her to sit down.

He finished off the letter he was writing, sanded it down and then, rising to his feet, came slowly across the room towards her.

'Well, young lady, I was wondering how long it would take you to pluck up enough courage to come here and apologise for your exceedingly foolish behaviour.'

'Apologise?' Verity echoed, slightly taken aback. Then she felt the first stirring of temper, and her finely arched black brows snapped together as she watched him seat himself in the chair opposite. 'On the contrary, Uncle Charles, if anyone ought to apologise it is you, for allowing me to believe that you hadn't taken the information I passed on to you seriously!'

He regarded her from beneath hooded lids. 'I rather think my colleague was right when he said that it's high time you were taken in hand.'

'If you are referring to that obnoxious individual you sent to Little Frampington, I should be obliged, when next you see him, if you tell him from me to keep his asinine views to himself!'

'Oh, dear.' There were definite signs of twitching about his lordship's mouth. 'It would appear you two had a slight difference of opinion when you met the other evening.'

'Difference of. . .? Ha! Yes, you might say that,' Verity concurred, controlling her temper with an effort. 'He's nothing but a brutish oaf!'

Lord Charles reached into his pocket and drew out a delicately painted enamel snuffbox. 'His opinion of you was not—how shall I put it?—over-complimentary, either. He was not best pleased to discover you had left the premises without him. Furthermore, he was halfway to convincing himself that you had made the whole thing up, and that no meeting had ever been arranged.'

'That isn't true, Uncle Charles!' Verity exclaimed, more hurt than angry now. 'I would never come to you with a mouthful of lies. You know I would not!'

'Yes, my dear. I do know,' he assured her without a moment's hesitation. 'I can only assume, therefore, that for some reason the meeting was cancelled, or that you misheard the time and place.'

'No, sir. I didn't. But what I did do was stupidly put my own interpretation on what was said,' Verity explained, looking rather shamefaced, and then went on to relate, verbatim, exactly what had passed between the spy and the man in the dark cloak.

Lord Charles listened intently, nodding in agreement when she voiced her belief that the meeting had in fact taken place at eight o'clock at the tavern at the first Frampington.

'Yes, child. You may possibly be right.'

'But that isn't all, sir. What is so confoundedly frustrating about the whole business is that I went to that tumbledown old tavern first. I didn't go inside,' she hurriedly assured him. 'One would need to take the precaution of being heavily armed before venturing into that place! But I did go into the stable, and in there I discovered a pair of fine greys harnessed to a racing curricle. It occurred to me at the time that it was a strange place for a gentleman of evident means to visit... And I saw that same turn-out in the park not an hour ago.'

He regarded her keenly, his shrewd grey eyes not wavering from her face. 'Can you be sure it was the same one?'

'Positive, sir. Perhaps both, but certainly one of those greys has a black diamond-shaped mark beneath its mane.'

'And do you happen to know the name of the person who was tooling the equipage?'

'Yes, sir.' She lowered her eyes. She didn't want to tell him, and yet she knew she must. 'It was a certain Major Brinley Carter.'

The hand raising a pinch of snuff to one of Lord Charles's thin nostrils checked for a moment. 'How very interesting.'

Something in his tone puzzled her, and she raised her eyes to look at him again. 'Do you happen to be acquainted with the Major, sir?'

'We've met, certainly,' he replied, returning his snuff-box to his pocket. 'Wellington speaks highly of him. A very brave man, by all accounts. Took a French Eagle in Spain. He was badly injured at Badajoz and was rewarded for his bravery with a Majority on his return to the Peninsula. Yes, a very brave man. Even the French, my dear, have a grudging respect for the men who wear rifleman-green.'

'I know of his exploits, sir,' Verity responded softly, a distinct catch in her voice. 'He is something of a local hero to the people of Yorkshire. And it wasn't easy for me to come here and tell you this. I thought the world of the Major's grandfather, Arthur Brinley, and although I'm forced to admit I have scant regard for Brin himself, I don't for one moment believe he would betray his country.'

'Many have done so, child. Money is a great incentive.'

'Yes, sir. And that is precisely why I cannot believe Brin is a traitor. His grandfather was a wealthy mill-owner and Brin has inherited that wealth. But. . .' a sigh escaped her '. . .I cannot help wondering what he was doing at Frampington last Friday evening at the appointed hour. Of course, there's always the possibility that he loaned the equipage to a friend for the evening, but. . .'

Giving a worried shake of her head, she rose to her feet. 'I had better be on my way, sir, otherwise Aunt Clara will be wondering what has become of me.'

'Thank you for coming here today, my child.' Lord Charles, ever the gentleman, rose also. 'Your information might prove extremely valuable.'

'I hope it does, and I should like nothing better than to be of some assistance to you.' She could not prevent a chuckle escaping at the dour look he cast her, but didn't hesitate to reassure him. 'I promise I shan't go careering about the country in the dead of night on my own again. But if there is anything I can do to help, anything at all, then I hope you won't hesitate to come to me.'

Lord Charles dined alone at his house that evening, and directly afterwards walked round to his club. Seating himself at one of the tables, he whiled away the time playing cards with several acquaintances, but his shrewd grey eyes, ever alert, frequently glanced over in the direction of the door to watch the other members come and go. As the evening wore on the rooms became more crowded, but the clock in the corner had chimed midnight before the gentleman he had been hoping to see put in an appearance.

Immaculately attired in a long-tailed black coat and tight-fitting buff-coloured pantaloons, which emphasised the rippling strength in his long, muscular legs, the gentleman strolled across the room and sat himself down at the only vacant table. Lord Charles finished the hand he was playing and, excusing himself, went over to the corner table.

'I was rather hoping that I might see you here tonight.' After calling to a waiter to bring a bottle and glasses, Lord Charles sat himself in the chair opposite and then looked his companion over. 'Been cutting a dash in Society again, I see. Where was it tonight, m'boy?'

'Lady Gillingham's soirée.' He raised his attractive eyes ceilingwards. 'I managed to sit through Miss Gillingham's appalling twanging on the harp, but when some ill-favoured rascal with a squint started mouthing out some rubbishing poem he had written, I was off!'

Lord Charles's shoulders shook. 'In different circumstances you might have got on very well with my niece Verity. She avoids such gatherings like the plague. And, talking of my little niece, she paid me a visit this afternoon.'

'Oh, aye?' Reaching for the burgundy the waiter had just deposited on their table, Lord Charles's companion poured out two glasses. 'What's the little monkey been getting up to now?'

'I get the distinct impression, m'boy, that my little

Verity remains firmly fixed in your black books. And I got the distinct impression earlier that she ain't overly fond of you, either.' He looked into the younger man's wickedly glinting eyes. 'What happened between you two at that inn at Little Frampington last week?'

'Obviously she didn't enlighten you?'

'No, she didn't. But she did tell me something rather interesting.'

His lordship wasted no further time in pleasantries, but disclosed what he had learned from his niece earlier. His companion listened intently, and when his lordship fell silent, said, 'So, she saw that equipage again today in the park. . . Who was tooling it, did she know?'

'That, m'boy, is the most interesting fact of all.' Lord Charles's smile was a trifle rueful. 'The gentleman handling the ribbons was none other than a Major Brin Carter.'

The younger man pursed his lips together in a silent whistle. 'You're right. That is interesting! And it might turn out to be the break we've been hoping for.'

'It might.' Lord Charles held the younger man's gaze steadily. 'And I imagine you can appreciate my rather invidious position. But what I must know is does the curricle and pair belong to the Major, and if so did he, in fact, lend the turn-out to a friend on the night in question?'

'Oh, it belongs to him, right enough,' his companion responded without a moment's hesitation and, delving into his pocket, drew out a folded piece of paper which he threw down on the table.

Lord Charles picked it up and, after running his eyes over it, raised a brow. 'Well, well! My little niece has turned up something well worth investigating.' He shook his head. 'Pity she ain't a boy. She's an observant little thing. I could have used her.'

'I, on the other hand, am very glad she isn't a boy. And I think it might be wise to give her a task to occupy her, if only to prevent her getting into more mischief.'

'What had you in mind?'

'Well, sir, it stands to reason that this—er—traitorous Major must be watched. And who better to perform that service than your delightful niece?'

Lord Charles gazed at his companion consideringly. 'What are you up to, m'boy?'

'Everything that is honourable, I assure you. You see, sir, it stands to reason that she'll need to be in the Major's company a great deal.'

'So, that's the way of it, is it?' Lord Charles raised his glass in a silent toast. 'Well, I wish you all the luck in the world in your pursuit of my niece. But I think I should warn you that she ain't overly fond of the Major, either.'

'You know, it's funny you should say that, because I got that distinct impression too. Some childish grudge, I expect. Still—' he shrugged '—she'll come round. I'll see to that, never fear!'

'I don't doubt it for a moment. And I don't doubt either that you'll make my niece an ideal mate.' Lord Charles's smile faded and his expression became thoughtful. 'But in the meantime be careful, m'boy. Verity's no fool. You might inadvertently let something slip, and if she gets wind of who owned that curricle and pair there's no saying what she may do... And I shouldn't be best pleased if harm ever came to her. I'm very fond of my little Verity.'

'Don't worry, sir. I'll take very good care of her. It'll

come as no great surprise, I'm sure, when I tell you that I'm more than just a little fond of the unruly minx myself!'

Chapter Six

Since their arrival in town Verity and her aunt had not spent above two evenings at home, and those had been through choice rather than a lack of invitations. Although Lady Billington was very gratified over this circumstance, and, indeed, over her niece's very compliant behaviour in agreeing to attend a wide variety of functions without so much as a quibble, she could not rid herself of the lowering feeling that Verity wasn't enjoying her first Season as much as she ought and that her niece's mind for the most part was quite otherwhere.

It came as something of a surprise, not to say a relief, therefore, when Verity betrayed genuine signs of enthusiasm over attending a party at Lady Morland's that evening. Lady Billington put this down to the fact that the hostess hailed from Yorkshire, and that her niece would be amongst people whom she knew well. Meg, who had been allowed more time to arrange the silky black locks in a riot of curls for the occasion, thought her young mistress's excitement stemmed from a desire to see the handsome gentleman who had drawn his curricle to a halt in the park the day before to speak to her.

In point of fact, neither was correct in her assumption. Verity had a keen desire to attend the occasion simply because of a note she had received earlier in the day.

Verity had always been a firm favourite with Lady Billington's servants. Not only was she easy to please, but she never made any unnecessary demands on their time. Since her sojourn in Curzon Street, however, she had rocketed in their estimation simply because she had taken it upon herself to walk their mistress's pampered and rather exacting Pekinese. Horace's morning jaunts to the unfashionable Green Park, where the cows grazed contentedly and the nursemaids took their boisterous charges for an airing, so contented the little dog that he was far less troublesome for the remainder of the day.

It was while Verity had been abroad in Green Park that morning that Lord Charles had paid an unexpected call on his sister. By the time Verity had returned to the house her uncle had already departed, but he had left a note for her:

> *My dear Verity,*
>   *I understand from your aunt that you are to attend a party at Sir Frederick Morland's house this evening, and I beg you will spare me a few moments of your time. I respectfully request that you meet me in the garden at ten o'clock, where I can speak to you in private.*
>   *Yours ever, C. H.*

The only possible reason for such a request that Verity could think of was that her uncle had some news to impart regarding the further progress of his vitally important investigations. It was obvious that he didn't wish his disclosures to be overheard—consequently this request for privacy.

Verity was overjoyed to think that her uncle trusted her enough to keep her informed of any progress. And if he trusted her enough for that, it wasn't beyond the realms of possibility that he might request her further help.

Her spirits soared at the prospect, and that evening she entered Lady Billington's carriage in high good humour, much to her aunt's delight. 'I'm so pleased you are looking forward to this evening, my dear. You must know Lady Morland quite well. Am I correct in thinking that she lived quite close to you before her marriage to Sir Frederick?'

'Yes.' Verity pulled a face. 'Too dratted close!'

Now that was most interesting! Lady Billington mused. So, Verity was not very fond of the lovely Lady Angela. Not that she was too concerned about this. Verity could be headstrong, and quite outspoken at times with people she knew well. And just what she got up to in the wilds of Yorkshire, Lady Billington dared not think! But not once had her niece given her cause to blush when in polite company. Her behaviour was always beyond reproach.

Consequently, when they arrived at their destination a short while later, Verity greeted her host and hostess graciously, not even by the blinking of an eye betraying the fact that she held Lady Morland in scant regard. Their hostess, on the other hand, looked Verity over rather keenly and for far too long, betraying, Lady Billington considered, a distinct lack of good breeding.

For the first hour Verity spent most of her time dancing. No matter where Lady Billington had chaperoned her niece, ball, rout or drum, Verity had never lacked for partners, and Lady Billington always experienced a deal of pride to see her graceful niece, never faltering over a single step, move about a dance-floor.

Sadly, though, since their arrival in town, Verity had been very impartial with her favours, and had never stood up with the same gentleman twice in any one evening. It came as no great surprise to Lady Billington, therefore, when Verity declined the invitation to dance again with the young gentleman who had claimed her hand not many minutes after their arrival, and remained quite contentedly seated beside her, staring about the crowded room.

'Where's Uncle Charles skulking, I wonder? I haven't set eyes on him at all this evening.'

Lady Billington didn't attempt to hide her surprise. 'Good heavens! I didn't realise he would be here. He never mentioned he would be attending when I saw him earlier today. Perhaps he's across the hall in the room set out for cards.'

Verity glanced at the rather ornate clock on the mantelshelf. It was a mere five minutes to the appointed meeting time. Her uncle was a stickler for punctuality and was in all probability already awaiting her in the garden, so she decided it was high time she was making her way there, too.

Informing her aunt that she was in urgent need of some liquid refreshment after all the dancing, she made her way across the room in the direction of a large table where a footman in livery was ladling out glasses of rather weak-tasting punch.

Having acquired the knowledge of how to gain access to the garden from a very informative young gentleman who knew the lay-out of the house, and who had partnered her earlier in a dance, Verity was now aware of the precise location of the door leading to the conservatory by which one gained access to the garden.

Secreting herself behind a conveniently placed potted palm, she peered through the foliage, cast her eyes about the room just to ensure no one was looking in her direction and, fairly confident that she wasn't being observed, slipped behind the plush velvet drapes.

The air in the conservatory struck cold after the warmth of the ballroom, bringing goose pimples to that bared portion of flesh between the long evening gloves and the ornate trimmings on the tiny puff sleeves of her lovely kingfisher-blue silk gown. She shivered as she took a surreptitious glance down the long glass-built construction, for it was not an uncommon occurrence to discover amorous couples stealing a few precious minutes alone in such places. Thankfully she detected no one lurking and, opening the door leading to the garden, stepped outside into the even cooler night air.

Lifting up her skirts a little, she risked taking a few steps along the gravel path, but dared not venture very far for fear of tripping and tearing her gown. The moon, hidden behind a veil of thin cloud, offered little light to aid her, but even so she could just detect the shapes of large shrubs on her left and what appeared to be a marble cherub holding an urn aloft.

She called her uncle's name softly, tentatively, but only an eerie silence answered her. Then, just as she was about to return indoors, fearing that Lord Charles had, perhaps, been unable to attend the party for some reason, she detected a sudden movement on her right and could clearly see a small red glow.

'Who is that? Who's there?' she demanded in a

voice that shook slightly, betraying alarm.

'Don't be afraid, lass.'

Every nerve in her body grew taut. She couldn't mistake that husky, accented voice, and was certain of who it was even before he stepped out of the shadows and she saw that now all too familiar tricorn and cloak. Unable to suppress a tiny squeal of sheer vexation, she swung round, but before she had taken more than a step or two back towards the conservatory he was already behind her.

Pulling her back against his broad expanse of chest, the Coachman captured her wrists and pinned her arms about her slender waist, holding them there securely with his own. 'Nay, lass, don't struggle so. Tha'll only end by tearing that very pretty gown o' yours,' he advised gently, but with more than just a hint of amusement in his voice, and Verity, never having been able, for some obscure reason, to control her emotions when in the company of this man, felt her temper stir.

'Then let me go, you—you barbarian!'

'Shh, now. Dusta want that lot inside to hear you and come out to investigate? I'd need t'op over t'wall right sharpish, and then tha won't hear what I've come 'ere especially t'tell you.'

'Well, what is it?' she snapped, her inability to break free bringing vividly to mind the humiliation she had suffered at his hands during their last encounter. More disturbing still was the effect his closeness was having on her pulse rate. He was so tall, so infinitely stronger than she was, that she would be powerless to prevent him from doing precisely what he wished to her, and yet that age-old feminine intuition assured her that he would never, ever do anything to cause her lasting harm.

'Wh-why did my uncle not come?' she prompted, trying desperately to ignore the warm breath, smelling faintly of tobacco, fanning her cheek.

''E 'ad an unexpected visitor turn up at 'is home, lass, and so sent a message for me t'come in 'is stead.'

'Then kindly pass on his message so that I can return inside!' Then, a little less sharply, 'It's cold out here.'

'Ain't I keeping tha warm, lass?' he husked against her left ear, before nibbling gently, and rather disturbingly, at the lobe.

'Stop that at once!' she snapped, trying desperately to ignore the delightful tingling sensation spreading down to her toes. 'Right from the start you've taken the most outrageous liberties with my person. You are no gentleman, sir!'

'Oh, I can be when I choose,' he returned blandly.

'Well, I've seen precious little evidence of it. In fact, you're the very worst kind of man. . . You're a bully!'

'Oh, I see. Tha's still smarting 'cause I walloped thy backside.' He paused for a moment, as though expecting her to admit to it, but she kept her lips firmly compressed. 'Nay, then, lass. That's the worst tha need ever fear from me. And tha deserved it! It were a damnably foolish thing tha did that evening, going out there by thissen. We're not dealing wi' a passel o' nursemaids.'

'I know that!' she retorted, far from appeased, and even farther from forgiving him for the humiliation she had suffered at his hands. 'I'm not an idiot!'

'Nay. Just a trifle spoilt,' he told her infuriatingly. 'But I still adore you.' He placed his cheek against the soft black curls. 'I can't stop thinking aboot thee, lass,' he astounded her by admitting. 'Tha's in m'blood. Never known a filly stir me t'way you do. And at least now I'll be able to see summat o' thee.'

Verity experienced such a maelstrom of diverse emotions that for several moments she was unable to think clearly. Anger and resentment still featured strongly, but she was feminine enough to experience a deal of gratification over his evident deep attraction to her. Curiosity, too, loomed large, and she decided that at this point in their rather short and somewhat torrid acquaintanceship curiosity was perhaps the safest feeling to betray, and so asked him outright why he felt they would be seeing more of each other.

'Well, if tha wants to 'elp 'is lordship and missen in our investigations, I don't see as 'ow tha can avoid it.'

Do you mean my uncle truly wants me to help?' Verity's most devout wish had been granted, and she experienced all the excitement of a child who had been promised a rare treat. 'But how? What does he want me to do?'

'T'information tha passed on t'Lord Charles about a certain major o' 'is acquaintance caused no little —er— interest, as tha might say. T'Major might well be completely innocent, o' course, but we needs to be certain. And that's where tha can 'elp.'

Verity didn't like the sound of this. No, she didn't like it at all. She had suffered agonising feelings of guilt after her last visit to her uncle. Surely something else hadn't been discovered about Major Carter?

'But how can I be of help?' she asked cautiously.

'I would o' thought that were obvious, lass. . . Tha knows 'im, dustn't tha?'

'I knew him, certainly.'

'Well, gets to know 'im all over again. Find out 'is movements. If tha discovers t'lad's attending a certain party of an evening, make sure tha's there, too. Be in 'is company as much as possible. Find out who 'is friends be and what 'e does wi' issen during the day. Be nice to 'im, friendly-like, and 'e may let one or two things slip out.'

'What?' Verity squealed, hardly daring to believe he was being serious. 'If I do that, Brin will think that I'm. . . He'll suppose that I'm—well—out to entrap him.'

'Well? And so you are, lass,' the Coachman pointed out, betraying his all-too-evident amusement once more.

'But not into marriage!' Verity countered hotly, but then began to turn the idea over in her mind. 'If I do this thing it will be for one reason only—to prove Brin's innocence, not his guilt.'

'Ah! So tha's a soft spot fer t'gallant Major Carter?'

'No, I have not!' The denial could not have been more forcefully spoken. 'The man's a buffoon! But I was very fond of his grandfather. And for Arthur Brinley's sake, I'll prove his grandson innocent.'

The Coachman was silent for what seemed an interminable length of time, and Verity sensed a change in him even before he said in a voice of such steely harshness that it brooked no argument, 'Very well, then. I'll permit thee to 'elp. But we'll 'ave certain matters clearly understood at the outset. Iffen tha should uncover summat— owt at all, no matter 'ow insignificant it might seem— tha's not to act upon it thissen but inform thy uncle at once. Occasionally tha'll be contacted by missen. I'll not always be in disguise, so tha must promise t'keep thy back towards me at all times, unless I tell you otherwise. 'Tis vital my identity remains a secret if we're to stand the remotest chance of catching this unscrupulous devil who's been passing information on to the French for a number of years.'

Verity nodded her head in agreement to all he had said before enquiring whether or not he had any idea who the traitor might be.

'Thanks to you, lass, we do now 'ave a possible lead. But I can say n'more for t'present.' And before she could even begin to ask whether he really did suspect Major Carter, he had placed his hands on her shoulders and had turned her round to face him squarely.

The muffler had been replaced by a hood. Eyes glinted wickedly down at her from behind slits cut in the leather, and it had been fashioned to leave the mouth exposed too. It gave him a rather sinister appearance, whereas before he had merely looked mysterious with his face well hidden behind the woollen scarf. Strangely, though, she experienced no fear.

It was strange, too, that it never occurred to her to struggle when he drew her closer, nor did she make the least attempt to turn her head away before his mouth fastened over hers.

Instinctively her lips parted beneath the seductive pressure of his own, and without conscious thought she raised her arms to entwine them round his neck. His response was immediate. A husky moan rose in his throat and he drew her body so firmly against his hard muscular frame that they seemed to meld together into one perfect whole, seemed inseparable, somehow. It was so strange, but still no thought of resistance entered her head. It was almost as though she belonged to him, body and soul, as though from birth she had been destined for this man alone, and nothing she said or did could detract her from this predetermined course. The very real possibility that this might be true didn't alarm her, for how could anything that felt so natural, so perfectly wonderful, be wrong?

Drawing his lips away, almost reluctantly, it seemed, he buried his face in her soft curls. ''Ere, lass, this won't do,' he murmured, his breathing ragged. 'I must keep a clear 'ead, but that's damnably 'ard when I'm intoxicated wi' the mere thought o' you. But when this is all over, when I'm free t'be wi' you, be very sure I'll never let tha go. Tha's mine, lass... Tha always were mine. I realise that now... And I'll never let another take thee from me.'

Only then did Verity experience a frisson of fear. Although he had spoken lightly there was no mistaking the raw determination in his voice. She knew he meant it, had meant every word; knew, too, that he was as powerless to resist her as she was to resist him. Then, as if to belie this, he held her away, and her eyes betrayed both uncertainty and fear.

'Nay, lass, don't look that way.' He ran his finger gently, reassuringly down her cheek. 'Everything will work out right fine.' He placed a swift, featherlight kiss on her forehead. 'Go now, while I still retain t'strength t'let you go. I'll wait right 'ere until tha's safe inside.'

Half of her didn't want to go, didn't want to leave him, and yet she knew she must while she still retained that tenuous hold on both mind and body. Everything was moving too quickly, and she needed time—time for reflection and consideration, time to interpret and understand the strangely mesmeric power this sometimes infuriatingly overbearing man seemed to have over her.

She didn't look back, but instinctively knew he was watching as she entered the conservatory, and then the room beyond. Thankfully many more people had arrived during the time she had been outside, and so she had little difficulty slipping unnoticed past the group standing near the curtain, and then wending her way across the room to where she had left her aunt.

'Good heavens, child! So there you are at last! I was just about to go searching for you. Where on earth have you been all this time?'

'I slipped outside for a breath of air.' She saw no reason to lie, and felt that in her present state of mind, in which strange, unfulfilled longings and a need to exercise common sense and control continued to vie for supremacy, she would make a pretty poor job of doing so if she tried. 'It's so very warm in here.'

It hadn't escaped Lady Billington's notice that her niece was looking rather flushed, but quite becomingly so. There was definitely an extra sparkle, too, in those blue eyes and; yes, her lips certainly did look a trifle swollen. If she didn't know better she would have suspected that Verity had been soundly kissed. Sadly, though, Verity hadn't a spark of romance in her anywhere. Rather a pity, really, she mused.

'In future, my dear, remember not to venture out on your own. One never knows who might be lurking.'

How very true! Nor how one will react, Verity reflected, with more than a touch of bewilderment, not to mention shame, at her wanton behaviour in the garden. Then she became aware that she was the focal point of a pair of rather piercing blue eyes, and asked her aunt who the tall and very handsome fair-haired gentleman was staring fixedly in her direction.

Lady Billington cast a brief glance across the room. 'Mr Lawrence Castleford. His uncle, Lord Castleford, knows your Uncle Charles very well, as a matter of fact. I believe Lord Castleford has something to do with the War Office, if my memory serves me correctly. He has one son, but it's common knowledge that he shows a distinct preference for that nephew of his. He really is a most unnatural father!'

Lady Billington then noticed their hostess making her way towards the exceedingly handsome Mr Castleford, and frowned slightly. 'Now, perhaps you would be kind enough to satisfy my curiosity over something. Why do you dislike Lady Morland?'

'I wouldn't go as far as to say I hold her in dislike, but I have scant regard for people of that ilk.'

'I do not perfectly understand, dear. I know she's only the daughter of a country squire, but I cannot imagine it's her birth at which you cavil.'

Verity couldn't prevent a rather wicked chuckle escaping. 'When you consider that one of the people I most admired was the peasant son of a whore, you might well be certain it isn't that.'

'Really, my dear!' Lady Billington shuddered. 'I wish you would learn to moderate your language.'

'I've heard Arthur Brinley described as far worse than that, I assure you.' A tender little smile curled her lips. 'One cannot help but admire a man who was born in the gutter, but who died one of the richest men in Yorkshire. One cannot help but admire anyone who strives, working all the hours God sends, to better himself. But I have scant regard for those who marry merely for social position.'

'Oh, I see!' Lady Billington cast a further glance in their hostess's direction, and then her eyes sought the rather portly figure of their host. 'So you think Lady Morland married merely for money?'

'No, I don't,' Verity hurriedly assured her. 'Had it been only for money I believe she would have married

Arthur Brinley's grandson. When I went to live in Yorkshire she and Brin were already, as one might phrase it,
seen as a couple.' Verity went on to explain. 'Angela
wouldn't have been much above sixteen then, and Brin
eighteen or nineteen. Everyone in the neighbourhood
thought they would eventually make a match of it. There
was a rumour at the time, and it wouldn't surprise me
to learn that it had been circulated by Angela herself,
that her parents would not give their consent to the match
until their daughter had attained her majority. Brin went
out to the Peninsula, and within three months Angela
had married her obese Baronet. And that occurred a year
before she had attained her majority.'

'So you think it was a title she was hankering after?'

'I certainly do, Aunt. As things have turned out, she
would have been wiser to have married the weaver's
spawn. She might any day now have found herself a
Viscountess!'

Verity's sudden gurgle of laughter drew several pairs
of eyes to turn in her direction, but she was oblivious to
the stares. 'And speak of angels!'

Once again Lady Billington found herself turning her
head in the direction of her niece's rather wickedly
amused gaze to see a tall, powerfully built figure standing
in the doorway. 'Good gracious, dear! Do you mean to
tell me that that most impressive young gentleman is
Arthur Brinley's grandson?'

'It is indeed!' She was unable to suppress a further
roguish chuckle. 'Just look at Brin Carter, a fine figure
of a man by anyone's standards, surely, and then look
at that great barrel of blubber Angela married. And if
you can sit there and tell me that she didn't marry for
social position, I shall think your wits are addled!'

'Well, quite!' was all Lady Billington would permit herself to utter. Unlike her niece, who never balked at plain speaking, she often considered it wisest to keep one's reflections to oneself, but secretly she thought Verity was probably quite right.

She studied the young Major intently as he made his way across the room. His bearing was certainly that of a military gentleman. He held himself very erect, and yet he moved with an athletic, fluid grace. Nature had certainly favoured him in both face and figure. His features were good, and although she could detect little, if any, resemblance to the Carter lineage, he exuded an air of impeccable breeding.

She could not quite understand from where her niece's dislike of the Major stemmed, for she felt certain there was some slight antipathy on Verity's part at least. She made a mental note to try to get to the root of this rather puzzling circumstance, for there was nothing at all in his demeanour, from what she could see, that would give one a distaste of him. And there was nothing in his manner either, she noted, as he reached his hostess's side, to betray the fact that he had once been very attached to Lady Morland.

He took her outstretched hand in his for a few brief moments, but if the lady expected him to play the gallant and kiss the tips of her fingers she was doomed to disappointment, for he merely executed an elegant bow before releasing his slight hold on her.

'I am so very pleased you accepted my invitation, Brin. It is wonderful to see you again after all these years.'

'I wouldn't have missed it for the world. It offers me the opportunity to thank you for the kindness you showed my grandfather by taking the trouble to visit him so often during my years away.' He interpreted her slight frown as reluctance to discuss her philanthropy and quickly changed the subject. 'You are looking well, Lady Morland. The years have been kind to you.'

She pouted prettily up at him, and he could not help thinking that on a girl of sixteen the look would have been appealing enough, but on a female in her mid-twenties it seemed rather ridiculous.

'Such reserve, sir! Am I to call you Major Carter?'

'If you wish it, madam. I think our former acquaint-anceship would permit a little less formality.'

'We were rather more than just acquaintances, Brin,' she reminded him in a husky, provocative voice, and raised limpid blue eyes in wide appeal. 'Have you still not forgiven me?'

The look in his own was hard to interpret. 'My dear, believe me, I bear you no ill-will. I have in recent years occasionally reflected on the rather fortunate circumstance that young ladies grow up more quickly than young gentlemen. Thankfully, you at least had the sense not to mistake close friendship for anything deeper. And for that alone I shall always be in your debt.'

This was not quite the response for which she had hoped. She looked at him keenly, believing his rather unflattering observations nothing more than a smoke-screen to hide a still bruised and battered heart, and was incensed to discover that he was not even looking at her now.

She turned her head in the direction of his openly admiring scrutiny, and her eyes narrowed. 'Ah! Do you remember little Verity Harcourt, Brin? What a hoyden she was, forever getting herself into some scrape or other. I recall your saying on more than one occasion what a spoilt little pest she was, forever following you about like some stray whelp.'

'Did I say that?' His brows snapped together. 'Well, I hope to God I had the sense not to say it to her face! Although. . .' His words faded and a rather twisted but not unpleasant smile curled his attractive mouth. 'Yes, that just might account for it!' he finished triumphantly, if rather enigmatically.

Verity hadn't missed the glances cast in her direction and couldn't help but wonder just what was being said about her. It crossed her mind that the Major, after their meeting in the park the previous day, might be considering asking her to dance, but if this had been his intention it was thwarted by Mr Castleford, who approached moments later requesting her to partner him in the next set of country dances.

She saw no earthly reason to refuse, even though she was impatient to begin her investigations into the Major's activities. According to her aunt, Mr Castleford was a firm favourite with the ladies, and to have refused him might have given rise to comment. And this was something that must be avoided at all costs, she knew. It was imperative, if she didn't wish to arouse suspicion, to act naturally at all times.

So, she continued to accept any gentleman's request to dance, but also ensured there were many occasions when she was seated by her aunt, thereby giving the Major numerous opportunities to approach her, but he made not the least attempt to do so. Frustration began to stir, and by the time the evening was drawing to a close she had become not just a little annoyed as well.

Guests began to depart and Lady Billington, who had enjoyed the evening enormously, suggested they too

should take leave of their host and hostess. Verity duti-
fully rose to her feet and, determined not to be thwarted
in her mission, weaved a path across the room, bidding
goodnight to her numerous acquaintances as she did so,
thereby trying to avoid rousing her aunt's suspicion by
taking such a circuitous route.

As she drew near the Major, who was standing with
his back towards her conversing with Lady Gillingham
and her pretty daughter, Verity quite deliberately jogged
his elbow. Unfortunately, half the contents of the glass
of champagne he happened to be holding ended down
the front of Miss Gillingham's very fetching primrose
silk gown, drawing forth a squeal from that hapless
damsel.

Verity's response was to utter an exclamation of dismay, which certainly didn't fool her aunt for a moment
and which, Lady Billington suspected by the slight narrowing of his attractive tawny-coloured eyes, had gone
no way to convincing the Major that it had been purely
an accident, either. But Lady Gillingham, thankfully,
seemed quite satisfied with Verity's rather prettily
worded apology and whisked her daughter away to effect
repairs.

'Wh-what an unfortunate accident!' Lady Billington
remarked heroically, stepping into the breach.

'Unfortunate, certainly,' was the Major's laconic
response, his gaze firmly fixed on what could best be
described as an unremorseful glint in a pair of violet-blue
eyes. 'Miss Harcourt, kindly do me the honour of introd-
ucing me to your gracious companion.'

Her niece complied, and Lady Billington found her
hand taken in a warm, firm clasp for a few moments. 'I
was slightly acquainted with your grandfather, Major,'

she remarked, deciding he had the most wonderful masculine smile she had ever seen. 'And may I offer you my very belated condolences on his sad demise. He was well respected, I know. Verity thought highly of him.'

There was a betraying twitch at the corner of the Major's finely chiselled lips. 'Yes, I recall your niece was a frequent visitor to our home in her formative years, ma'am. My grandfather had the reputation of being a strict disciplinarian, but he certainly mellowed with age. Surprisingly, your niece's frequently wayward behaviour, far from arousing his wrath, rather amused him.'

Out of the corner of her eye Lady Billington saw her niece stiffen, and once again stepped into the breach. Voicing the hope that they would meet again soon, she bade the Major a hurried farewell, and then whisked her niece away before Verity could compound her reprehensible actions of minutes before by saying something cutting in retaliation to the major's rather unfortunate reminiscences.

'I wonder at you sometimes, child!' she chided, once they were safely ensconced in her carriage. 'You jogged Major Carter's elbow on purpose.'

Verity made not the least attempt to deny it. Although she was seething with anger over Brin's rather uncalled-for remarks, the incident as a whole had not been without its amusing side. 'I didn't intend that he should throw the contents of his glass over Clarissa Gillingham. What a widgeon the girl is, setting up such a screech over nothing!'

'I never for one moment suspected that that was your intention, child. What eludes me completely is why you should have gone out of your way to speak to someone you hold in contempt.'

Verity was unable to meet her aunt's rather searching look, and turned her head to stare resolutely out of the window.

'We Harcourts do not appreciate being ignored,' she remarked loftily. 'The wretch never made the least attempt to approach me, but he most certainly found the time to speak to most every other young female in the room!'

There was more than just a hint of pique in her voice, and Lady Billington could not help but feel that her lovely young niece was not as indifferent to the handsome Major as she imagined herself to be. She could not help but wonder, too, what the Major thought now of the girl whom he had, evidently, on occasions found something of a nuisance years ago. There was no denying that he had made not the least attempt to speak to Verity, but Lady Billington had caught him glancing quite frequently in her niece's direction.

There had been something rather more than just appreciation in his gaze; something that at this early stage she decided it might be rather foolish to try to interpret. Furthermore, far from the buffoon Verity was so fond of calling him, Major Brin Carter was an intelligent man. In fact, just the man, unless she was very much mistaken,' to keep her occasionally wayward niece firmly under control.

A twitching smile of contentment pulled at the corners of her mouth as she leaned against the plush velvet squabs. The future, she mused, was set fair to become not only intriguing, but highly promising too!

Chapter Seven

If Lady Billington had hoped that the foundations of her niece's possible future happiness would be laid without delay, she was doomed to disappointment. Long before she and Verity had risen to begin a new day of frivolous enjoyment, Major Carter had already left London.

Travelling west, Brin tooled his curricle along the main post road to Oxford. It was such bliss to be in the country again after several weeks of breathing the stale air of the capital. And how he disliked town life! How the endless round of social gatherings, where each hostess vied with the other for that supreme accolade of having held the 'Event of the Season,' was already rapidly beginning to pall!

He was invited everywhere. A party was not considered even a moderate success if Major Brin Carter did not attend. The pile of invitation cards back in the library at Berkeley Square grew daily and the door-knocker was never still. But how many of those who now fawned about him, turning his stomach with their fulsome praises and falsely fixed-on smiles, would have given him a second look if he were not destined to be the next Viscount Dartwood?

A wry smile curled his lips. Thank God he had inherited his grandfather's sound judgement and no-nonsense common sense! Otherwise the attention he had been receiving of late might well have turned his head.

Perhaps he had not always behaved as wisely as he might have done. There had been instances in the past where, were it possible to relive, he would certainly behave differently. He had made mistakes—damned foolish ones too!—but then, who hadn't? Thankfully, though, he was a deal more discerning now than he had been in his youth.

Perhaps he had become a trifle cynical, too. That undoubtedly was the result of his years in the army, when one had had to learn to live one day at a time, never planning too far ahead. One had never known whether one would return from a mission, but one had swiftly learned whom one could trust or not. He had known both good and bad officers, both good and bad men in the lower ranks, and it was no different with those whom he had left behind in London.

Some were genuine; some most certainly were not. And there was a time, he reminded himself, when, not so discerning, he would have stigmatised all those well-bred females of Society as designing harpies and all the so-called gentlemen as mindless coffee-house fops. Five years before he would never have believed it possible that he would eventually consider a man coming from the highest echelon in Society as his most trusted friend.

He arrived at his friend's country estate early in the afternoon. The mansion, built in stone of burnished gold, was surrounded by many acres of fine rolling parkland. The main driveway swept down in a graceful arc and at its highest point offered panoramic views of the Oxfordshire countryside.

Ravenhurst was a magnificent sight by any standard. The park, laid out by 'Capability' Brown during the previous century, with its sweeping lawns, clumps of stately trees and its well-stocked trout stream and lake, was a feast to the eye. At the rear of the building was the formal garden, sectioned off by neat box hedges and criss-crossed by weed-free gravel paths. Beyond that, and spreading to either side of the building, was the shrubbery, where rhododendrons when in full bloom added such vibrant splashes of rich colour to the wonderful setting that its beauty almost took one's breath away.

Brin could never come to Ravenhurst without remembering vividly the first time he had stayed at this awe-inspiring country estate. A few short weeks after he had rejoined his Regiment in the Peninsula, Wellington had taken the French-held city of Badajoz. Badly wounded in the siege, Brin had been carried back to camp on a stretcher. The army surgeon had taken one look at the festering wound in the young Captain's side and had not attempted to remove the deeply embedded lead shot.

Brin had then been placed with the dead and dying. His name would most certainly have been added quite swiftly to the long, long list of fatalities had it not been for the actions of his commanding officer, who had taken it upon himself to convey the gallant young Captain back to England where, if the worst should happen, he could at least be buried in his native Yorkshire and not be placed in some nameless grave in Spain.

Colonel Pitbury had not expected Brin to survive the rigours of the overland journey to the port. The civilian doctor who had been on board the vessel bound for Southampton, and who during the voyage had removed the ball from Brin's side and also the one lodged in his shoulder, had not expected his patient to survive. By the time they had docked in Southampton Brin's body had been racked with fever, but still he had held on to those tenuous threads of life. But for how much longer?

Colonel Pitbury had been in a quandary, not wishing to place this gallant young officer in the hands of strangers and yet fearing that Brin couldn't possibly continue to survive if he was forced to make the long journey by coach back to his native Yorkshire. Then he had recalled a letter which had come into his possession, addressed to the young Captain from a certain Mr Marcus Ravenhurst.

Of course Colonel Pitbury had not known that Captain Carter and Marcus Ravenhurst far from being friends had been barely acquainted; that they had merely found themselves earlier that year stranded at the same wayside inn for a few days. He had only experienced untold relief when, upon arrival at the vast Oxfordshire estate, the lady of the house, without the least hesitation, had ordered the Captain brought in from the post-chaise. But as the Colonel had stood there watching Brin, his young body limp, his wounds still festering, being carried by four burly footmen up the wide sweeping staircase, he had believed he was seeing him for the last time. But Colonel Pitbury had not taken into account the sheer determination and unfailing devotion of Sarah Ravenhurst.

Brin's eyes suddenly grew misty with unshed tears as memory flooded back. So deep in the throes of fever, he had been sublimely unaware of the sea voyage, let alone his arrival at this beautiful place. The first thing he had seen when the fever had broken had been the smiling face of a lovely angel peering down at him.

And Sarah Ravenhurst *was* an angel, a loving wife and mother and the most loyal surrogate sister any man could ever wish for. She had not only healed his body three years ago, but also his mind.

He now found it difficult to believe just what an embittered young man he had been in those days. Crossed in love, and for years having been castigated as weaver's spawn, or worse, by the sons of so-called gentlemen, he had become resentful and disillusioned. But his weeks convalescing at Ravenhurst had changed all that. By the time he had left England to rejoin his regiment in Spain he had been made to appreciate his own worth.

Ashamed though he was to admit it, there had been a time when the mere thought of entering the ranks of the nobility would have terrified him, but that was no longer the case. He had proved himself to be an excellent soldier, a natural leader of men, and given time he would prove himself to be a considerate landlord and a respected member of the peerage. And he owed this confidence, this belief he now had in himself, to Marcus and Sarah Ravenhurst.

After drawing his curricle to a halt in the stable yard, and exchanging a few playful punches with Sutton, the head groom, he went round to the front entrance and was admitted by his friends' very correct butler, Stebbings, who informed him that the mistress was in the small parlour and the master was busily working in the library.

'In that case I'll inflict my company upon your mistress,' Brin told him, handing over his hat and coat. 'But,' he added, prompted by an imp of pure devilment, 'be good enough not to delay too long in informing your master of my arrival.'

He opened the parlour door to find Sarah Ravenhurst seated by the window, busily plying her needle. After a few moments she looked round to see who had entered. There followed a shriek of delight as the sewing was tossed aside and she came rushing forward to be enfolded in a pair of welcoming arms.

'Oh, Brin, it's lovely to see you!' The deep affection she bore him was mirrored in her lovely aquamarine-coloured eyes. 'Is it just a passing visit or will you be staying?'

'Kindly unhand my wife, sir!' a deep masculine voice ordered from the doorway before Brin could open his mouth to reply. 'You're never here above five minutes before you're making love to Sarah!'

'Yes, very true,' that incorrigible damsel responded, not making the least attempt to break free from the Major's hold. 'I'd call him out if I were you.'

'Good God, madam! Do you want to be a widow? He was one of the finest marksmen in the British Army, if not the finest.' Abandoning his affronted pose, Marcus Ravenhurst, one brow arching mockingly, came forward to grasp his friend's hand. 'Town life not to your taste, eh?'

At the pained look on his face both husband and wife dissolved into laughter. 'Yes, you can mock, both of you. Heaven spare me! It's enough to send a sane soul distracted.'

'I must confess attending the endless round of parties does tend to become a trifle tedious after a time,' Sarah agreed, entwining her arm round Brin's and guiding him over to the sofa. 'But what can one do? One is forced to accept invitations, otherwise one is liable to give offence.'

'There are quite a number I should take the greatest pleasure in offending,' Brin told them roundly. 'I've blessed you time without number these past weeks, Marcus, for writing that letter of introduction to Jackson's Boxing Salon. It's such a relief to get away from those matchmaking mamas, if only for a short time.'

'Bound to have happened. You're hot property at the moment, a very eligible *parti*.' Marcus handed Brin a glass of Madeira before seating himself in the chair opposite. 'I must teach you how to affect a withering look. That will relieve you of any unwanted attentions. Always worked for me!'

'He doesn't need to fall into any of your bad habits,' Sarah put in, casting her husband a disapproving glance. 'I'm sure he's more than able to cope.' She turned her attention on Brin once more, with that wicked twinkle in her eyes which he loved so much. 'I cannot believe that not one of those highly finished articles hasn't taken your fancy, Brin.'

'Two or three have, as it happens. And that is why I'm here.' Pausing to sample the excellent wine, he leaned back against the soft upholstery of the sofa. 'You have been more than generous already, allowing me the use of your town house, and I know I shouldn't ask it of you, Sarah, so soon after giving birth to Julia, but I was wondering if you would be good enough to permit me to invite a party here, of not more than eight people, in the not too distant future?'

'Of course I don't mind!' she didn't hesitate to assure him. 'You mustn't pay any attention to Marcus. He fusses so. I suffered no ill effects after little Hugo's birth, and it has been no different with Julia's. I'm as fit as a fiddle and would have been happy to join you for a few weeks in Berkeley Square. But, as you very well know, I was foolish enough to marry a dictatorial creature who will have none of it, and who insists on protecting me as though I were as fragile as thistledown.'

'And I would behave just the same if you were mine.' Brin smiled at her tenderly. 'Not many men are as fortunate as Ravenhurst. But at least a man ought to do all he possibly can to ensure that he has made the right choice in a wife. And that is precisely why I wish to invite certain young ladies here.'

Sarah's ears pricked up at this. 'Oh?'

'I have singled out three who I think would be admirably suitable for a future viscountess.' He fixed his gaze on an imaginary spot on the richly coloured carpet. 'But I mistook a lady's feelings, a lady's true nature, once before, remember? And I have no intention of making that very foolish mistake again.'

Sarah's smile faded and a hint of sadness crept into her eyes. She knew all about Brin's boyhood sweetheart and how bitterly hurt he had been when he had discovered she had married Sir Frederick Morland. 'Do—do you still think about Angela, Brin? Does she still retain a place in your affections?'

'Good gracious, no!' There was no mistaking the conviction in his voice. 'Of course I shall never forget her kindness to my grandfather. She continued to visit him regularly, even after she had married. I never received a letter from him without his mentioning that 't'lass has been here again'. It was a wonderful thing she did, giving up so much of her time to be with a dying old man, and

I shall always be beholden to her for that, but. . .'

His words faded and he paused to take a further sip of Madeira. 'Strangely enough, last night I saw her for the first time since her marriage, when I attended a party at her house. I thought I'd feel something, and yet, Sarah, the only thing I experienced was relief that I hadn't been foolish enough to marry her.'

'You are not the first man to have allowed his heart to rule his head,' Marcus put in gently, 'and I doubt you'll be the last.'

'And that is precisely why I have no intention of making that very foolish mistake again. It is one thing to see someone for an hour or two at a party, and quite another to be in that certain someone's company for a considerable length of time, when one might observe certain—er—defects in a character which might not otherwise be apparent.'

Sarah regarded him in silence for a moment, then said, 'You say three young ladies have taken your eye. Have you truly no preference?'

'No, they are all equally charming.' Brin suddenly raised his eyes from their further contemplation of the patterned carpet. 'Oh, did I say three? Actually, there's a fourth. Unfortunately, though, she poses one or two slight problems. She frequently doesn't behave as she ought.'

Sarah exchanged a meaningful glance with her spouse. 'Well, of course, Brin, invite whomever you like. But, in the meantime, I assume you will be staying with us for at least one night?' At his nod of assent she rose to her feet. 'In that case I shall instruct that your bedchamber is made ready for you.'

Marcus gazed fixedly into the contents of his glass

until the door had closed behind his wife, then raised his
eyes to stare directly into those of his friend. 'If you
imagine for one moment that Sarah believed that bag of
moonshine, then your weeks in London have addled your
wits, m'boy.'

'No, of course I don't think it. But I also know she
would never attempt to pry.'

'Very true, she would not.' Marcus continued to hold
his friend's gaze steadily. 'But I am quite a different
proposition. Now, without further roundaboutation, may
I be permitted to know the real motive behind your
request?'

Verity, seated at the escritoire in the sunny front parlour
overlooking the street, was trying her best to compose a
letter to her uncle Lucius. In the normal course of events
she would have had no difficulty in writing an account
of her doings in London to her guardian, but her mind
flatly refused to concentrate on the task and kept dwelling
on the possible whereabouts of a certain Major of her
acquaintance.

Brin had been away from London a full two weeks.
Someone had spotted him tooling his curricle and pair
on the main road to Oxford the day after the Morlands'
party. This in itself had given little cause for concern.
After all, his close friends the Ravenhursts resided in
Oxfordshire. What could be more natural than for him
to have paid them an impromptu visit?

Her eyes narrowed as she stared blindly out of the
window. What was not so easy to understand, however,
was what he had been doing two days later, travelling
along the Great North Road. His eventual destination, of
course, might well have been Yorkshire, but even so it

was rather an odd time to decide to pay a visit to his home, just when the Season was beginning to get in full swing.

More puzzling still had been Lord Charles's attitude to the Major's sudden and unexpected absence from town. And there was no doubt in Verity's mind that Brin's decision to leave London had been made on the spur of the moment, because he had been expected to attend several functions and had arranged for notes of apology to be sent to those hostesses concerned for his unavoidable absence. But when Verity had explained this to her uncle, and had then gone on to inform him that she had learned from a very reliable source that the Major had been seen three days after his departure from London alighting from a hired post-chaise at an inn near Newark, Lord Charles had seemed sublimely unconcerned.

'I do not think there is any reason for us to be uneasy over that, my dear,' he had said, with a shrug that only confirmed his complete indifference. 'If it was, indeed, the Major alighting from that carriage, it is more than likely he intended paying a visit to his home.'

'That occurred to me, sir. But why do so now? After all, he has been back in England for several weeks. Surely it would have made more sense to pay a visit to Yorkshire before the Season had begun?' Verity had remained suspicious. 'There's something decidedly smoky about his behaviour.'

'You may possibly be right, dear. But don't let us jump to conclusions. When he eventually returns, see if you cannot uncover the reason behind his unexpected departure from town. But, as I've already mentioned, there is no reason for us to be unduly concerned. I do know the precise whereabouts of our little French friend,'

Lord Charles had gone on to say, 'and have people watching his lodgings twenty-four hours a day. He has made no attempt to leave London, so we can be fairly certain that no information has been handed over to him as yet.'

So, Verity had left her uncle's house having to be satisfied with that. But the simple fact remained that she had been far from happy. And she still wasn't happy. Brin's behaviour was, to put it mildly, most odd, and her uncle's attitude, too, gave her cause for concern. If she didn't know better she would swear that Lord Charles was completely uninterested in Major Carter. But if that was the case, why then had he asked her to keep an eye on him?

The door-knocker echoing round the hall broke into her perplexing thoughts and a few moments later the butler, looking decidedly disapproving, entered the parlour to inform her that a gentleman had called to see her.

Verity raised her eyes heavenwards. Almost from her arrival in town she had been plagued by an endless stream of young men calling at her aunt's house. She ought, she supposed, to be flattered by all the attention she was receiving, and in a way she was, but she was in no danger of losing her heart to any one of them. That did not mean, however, that she would deliberately go out of her way to hurt any young gentleman's feelings, and for this reason she had never refused to receive a caller. But she was swiftly coming to the conclusion that displaying impartiality in order to avoid arousing false hopes in any one of her many young admirers was the totally wrong tactic to adopt.

'His name, Watts?'

'His name, Miss Harcourt, is Carter,' a deep voice answered from the doorway, and it took every ounce of

self-control Verity possessed not to gape across at the
Major as he strolled, uninvited, into the room. It really
was most uncanny. Whenever she spoke or thought about
him he seemed to appear from nowhere!

'Why, Major! What a pleasant surprise!' The smile of
welcome hid quite beautifully her astonishment as she
rose from the escritoire and moved slowly towards him.
'I understood you were out of town.'

He slanted a mocking glance. 'Keeping tabs on me,
Miss Harcourt?'

'Not at all, Major.' Her trill of laughter sounded affected even to her own ears. 'But your absence from town
has been remarked upon from time to time, and has cast
certain young ladies into the mopes.'

'But by your beautiful bloom I can safely assume that
you are not similarly afflicted, Miss Harcourt.'

Definitely I'm not! Verity thought, only just stopping
herself from retorting that she would never repeat her
foolishness of years before by growing fond of him. He
had hurt her once, and she would never offer him the
opportunity of doing so again!

'How could I possibly be one of them, sir,' she
responded, her smile nowhere near reaching her eyes.
'You and I have known each other for years. Why, we
are more like brother and sister!'

If her intention had been to dent his masculine pride
it was obvious she had fallen far short of the mark,
for his immediate response was, 'Just what I've been
endeavouring to explain to this excellent servant of your
aunt's. But, as he quite correctly pointed out, it is most
improper for you to entertain a gentleman caller indoors,
unchaperoned. So, might I suggest that as it's such a

pleasant morning we go for a turn in the park in my curricle?'

Even though spending the smallest amount of time in his company was abhorrent to her, Verity could not let this golden opportunity to begin her inquisition slip away and hurriedly accepted the invitation.

Delaying only for the time it took her to don a very becoming bonnet, she accompanied him outside into the late April sunshine to discover the curricle awaiting them, the heads of those unmistakable greys being held by a young groom.

'What superb horses these are!' Verity remarked, after the Major had ordered the groom to return to Berkeley Square and had given the pair their office to start.

'Indeed they are, Miss Harcourt.'

'I cannot recall ever having seen you tool an equipage before you joined the army.' There was no response. 'If my memory serves me correctly you used to ride almost everywhere.'

'And I still do ride frequently.' She didn't miss the quizzical glance he cast her. 'But when in town I believe it is expected of one to —er—cut a dash.'

'So you purchased them to cut a figure in Society, sir?'

'Not entirely, no.'

The horses, then, certainly did belong to him. Discovering this was a start, but there was still a great deal more she had to uncover. 'Have you had them long? How does one go about acquiring such handsome beasts?'

'My, my! What a lot of questions you do ask, Miss Harcourt! Anyone would imagine that your sole purpose for accepting my invitation was to interrogate me.'

Brin was far more astute than she had remembered. She must tread more warily from now on, she decided, casting him a sweet smile. 'No such thing, Major! It was only that I rather have a fancy for driving myself about town. It is not only the gentlemen that cut a dash, you know.'

'True. But don't expect me to encourage you in such folly.' Determination hardened his voice, striking a chord of memory, but before Verity could capture the fleeting remembrance he was speaking again, in his normal, pleasant tone.

'Your Uncle Lucius would never forgive me. And, talking of your uncle, he asked me to pass on his regards.' He couldn't mistake the sudden gleam of satisfaction which brightened her eyes for one unguarded moment. 'Yes, Miss Harcourt, I have been in Yorkshire.' His lips twitched. 'Now, aren't you going to enquire what took me there?'

After counting up to ten very slowly under her breath, Verity said, 'No. And I have no intention, either, of seeking your assistance in acquiring a pair of horses, because I've just remembered that Tattersall's is the place to go!'

'Not for a lady, it isn't,' he countered.

'Then how the deuce does a female go about buying a decent pair?' Verity demanded, annoyed at the rather stupid codes of conduct thrust upon young, unmarried females.

'I see you haven't yet learned to control that rather naughty temper of yours, Miss Harcourt,' he told her infuriatingly. 'I recall my grandfather saying years ago that you needed a firmer hand than Lucius Redmond possessed.'

Verity regarded his very attractive profile with narrowed, assessing eyes. For some perverse reasons best known to himself he was deliberately baiting her. Well, she wouldn't let him come out the victor from this little encounter!

'Come, come, Major Carter. You know that is a complete untruth. I recall quite clearly your saying, the very last time we met, that your grandfather looked upon me with a very indulgent eye and found my little ways quite winning.'

'*Touché*, Miss Harcourt!' he acknowledged, with such an appreciative smile that Verity found her ill-humour ebbing away. 'And if I were you, I would certainly find someone to advise you who knows a deal about horse-flesh before you even think of attempting to purchase your own cattle.'

'Is that what you did, Major?' she couldn't resist asking, out of sheer devilment and not any real desire to learn more.

'Yes, in a way. My very good friend Marcus Ravenhurst knew I was looking out for a pair and put me in the way of these fine animals.'

Did he, now? Most interesting! Verity would dearly have liked to know precisely when the Major had acquired the superb greys, but, given that he was already suspicious of her many questions, she refrained from enquiring and merely remarked in a conversational way, after he had tooled his team expertly through the park gateway, whether he intended staying in London for the remainder of the Season.'

'I've no fixed plans, Miss Harcourt. Much depends, of course, on circumstances.'

'By that, do you mean the viscountcy?'

'Yes, but there are -er- certain other considerations,' he responded, keeping his gaze firmly fixed on the carriage path ahead. 'Ah! I do believe that is Lady Gillingham and her delightful daughter.'

The Major drew his team to a halt beside the Gillinghams' open barouche. After greetings had been exchanged, Verity listened to the brief conversation which passed between Gillingham and Brin and had to own that his address was faultless.

There was no denying, either, that he exuded an air of quiet but unimpeachable breeding. Had he always possessed this rather charming and dignified manner? she wondered, her eyes glancing fleetingly at Clarissa who seemed in an unusually subdued frame of mind, merely responding with a 'yes' or 'no', or 'indeed, Mama' when addressed directly.

'I hope to see you at our ball tomorrow evening, Miss Harcourt,' Lady Gillingham remarked, drawing Verity's attention.

'I shouldn't miss it for the world, ma'am,' she assured her. 'I am reliably informed that your floral decorations are unsurpassed and that you do not conform to the present unfortunate vogue for transforming a ballroom into a silk tent.'

'I can safely promise I shan't do that. And, unless you have further urgent business which is likely to call you away, Major Carter, I look forward to your company as well.' And with that she gave her coachman the order to move on.

'What a very pleasant woman Lady Gillingham is,' Brin remarked as he too moved off. 'She has such charming, unaffected manners. It's a thousand pities there aren't more of her ilk gracing Society.'

'Yes, indeed,' Verity agreed. 'And Clarissa is very like her, but she was certainly out of sorts today. She barely uttered a word.' Eyes suddenly brimful with mischief, she cast him a sidelong glance. 'I wonder if she's still a little peeved with you for throwing that glass of champagne over her at the Morlands' party?'

Brin would have been the first to admit that he had taken very little interest in Verity before he had left Yorkshire to join the army five years ago, considering her nothing more than a very pretty but decidedly spoilt child. But he had seen enough of her in her formative years to recognise that particular look and, furthermore, to know precisely what it signified.

'I shall take leave to inform you, Miss Verity Harcourt, that you are an unprincipled little baggage!'

Far from offended, Verity gurgled with laughter. 'I admit, I have been known to behave a little —er—unconventionally at times. But unprincipled. . .? Never!'

From that moment Verity felt completely at ease in his company, just as she had done years ago, when he had behaved towards her like some indulgent elder brother. So relaxed and contented did she become that by the time they had arrived back at Curzon Street, and she was alighting from the curricle, she was not perfectly sure whether she had agreed so readily to save him a dance at Lady Gillingham's ball because it offered the ideal opportunity to quiz him further, or simply because she genuinely wanted to be with him.

Chapter Eight

To say that Verity took little pride in her appearance would be to do the girl, Lady Billington considered, a gross injustice. Although her niece, compared to many other young ladies, spent a relatively short amount of time over her toilet, she always managed to look well-groomed. She did, however, have an unfortunate tendency to select rich, vibrant colours for her clothes: reds, dark greens and, of course, deep blues, her particular favourite. So it had come as something of a relief to Lady Billington when Verity had left the choice of materials for new gowns to her.

Of course, pastel shades were considered the only suitable colours for young, unmarried females, and Lady Billington considered it as something of an achievement to see her niece going about London dressed in pale primrose, pale blue or pink, but her greatest triumph of all, she considered, was persuading Verity to have at least one evening gown of purest white, a colour her niece had always steadfastly refused ever to consider wearing.

Lady Billington experienced no little satisfaction,

therefore, when they arrived at the Gillinghams' ball on
Thursday evening. Looking particularly ethereal in a
gown of white spider gauze over a white satin petticoat,
with a spray of white flowers nestling in her beautifully
arranged raven locks, Verity drew no little attention as
they entered the crowded ballroom, but as usual she
seemed oblivious to the many admiring glances cast in
her direction.

'I must say, Aunt Clara, you were absolutely right,'
Verity announced unexpectedly as they seated themselves on two of the spindle-legged chairs placed against
the wall.

'About the dress, do you mean? I know, dear. You
look enchanting.'

'I'm not talking about that!' Verity responded with an
impatient wave of her hand. 'I meant the flowers. You
said Lady Gillingham's arrangements were the finest
you've ever seen. And I must say they are outstanding.'

'Indeed, yes. And I do believe she does them all
herself.'

'Then she's extremely gifted. I wish I could achieve
a result half so lovely.'

Lady Billington was not offered the opportunity to
respond, for a young gentleman, sporting a dazzling
green-and-yellow-striped silk waistcoat, approached
them and whisked Verity away to join the couples taking
up positions for the first set of country dances.

She followed their progress across the floor, smiling
to herself. Her niece was, fundamentally, a sweet-natured
girl, very generous and genuine in her praise. There was
no denying, though, that Verity had on occasion allowed
her temper to get the better of her, and she certainly didn't
suffer fools gladly, but Lady Billington could never recall

her niece deliberately hurting someone's feelings without having had very good reason. She was as happy talking with stable-boys as dukes, and had never been known to look down upon those less fortunate than herself, which certainly did the girl great credit. But Lady Billington was not blind to her niece's faults. The girl could be quite stubbornly headstrong at times and would need a man with as strong a will as her own, if not stronger, to keep her in check.

Her attention was suddenly drawn to the doorway, and she watched the entrance of two new guests. It was not her brother's unexpected appearance which brought a rather satisfied smile to her lips, however, but the arrival of the tall gentleman standing beside him. Now there was someone, unless she was very much mistaken, more than equal to the task of keeping a tight rein on a headstrong filly!

Verity was unaware of the arrival of Lord Charles and Major Carter, for at that precise moment she was moving down the floor, concentrating hard on the intricate steps. She was not allowed to return to her seat once the dance came to an end, for her hand was claimed by a second young gallant and then directly afterwards by a third. She began to think that, unless she took some drastic action, she was in the gravest danger of spending the whole evening on the dance-floor. So, as soon as that particular set came to an end, she neatly avoided a fourth young gentleman who looked perilously as if he was heading in her direction by making a bee-line for a young footman holding several glasses of champagne on a silver tray.

She quickly discovered she wasn't the only one in urgent need of refreshment. No sooner had she relieved the footman of one of the glasses than a small, slender figure appeared at her side and promptly did the same.

'Yes, it is getting rather warm in here, and rather crowded,' Verity remarked. 'Although, I'm certain my aunt would say that that is a definite mark of success. Your mama must be very satisfied with the evening so far,' she went on when she received no response. 'And the flower arrangements are the most outstanding I've ever seen.'

'Mama is very gifted in so many things.' A tiny sigh escaped Clarissa. 'I wish I could be more like her.'

Although they had never met before the Season had begun, they had always exchanged friendly words whenever they had been attending the same party of an evening, so Verity didn't consider it vulgarly forward to say, 'But you are very like her, Miss Gillingham. Many people have remarked upon it.'

'In looks, yes. But Mama is so very polished. She always looks so elegant, so poised, no matter in whose company she happens to be, whereas I. . .'

'You appear equally so, Miss Gillingham.'

'Please call me Clarissa,' she said with a shy smile. 'I do try to behave as Mama would wish, but I sometimes make a complete mull of it. I feel much more at ease in the country. I love being with Papa, helping at the home farm.'

Verity was astonished by the admission. She found it difficult to envisage such a fragile-looking creature stomping through inches of dirt and mud in serviceable boots, but evidently it was what she preferred to do.

'Mama was so looking forward to bringing me out,' Clarissa continued with a plaintive little sigh. 'She has worked so hard to make it all a success, and I dearly hope that I do not disappoint her by not achieving a suitable match, but. . .'

'I'm sure you won't disappoint her.' Verity's smile was reassuring. 'No matter where I've seen you, your company is always being sought by many young gentlemen.'

'I know,' Clarissa responded with scant enthusiasm. 'The trouble is, though, I find it difficult to converse with many of them. All they seem to think about is the latest fashion in coats or footwear—silly, unimportant things like that. Even Major Carter, whom I like above any other, doesn't seem to know very much about farming.'

Verity managed to control a quivering lip, but it was an effort. 'No, I don't suppose he does. Major Carter, after all, chose a career in the army, not one working on the land. Although,' she added with a generosity which would have astounded her aunt, 'I expect if he turned his mind to it he would make a success of land management.'

She paused to sip her champagne, her eyes moving about the room. 'Heavens above! Wonders will never cease! Uncle Charles is here. Will you excuse me, Clarissa? I must return to my aunt, otherwise she'll be wondering what has become of me.'

Lady Billington had not been in the least concerned over Verity's long absence, for she had been keeping half an eye on her niece throughout the whole period that she had been away from her side. She had managed to keep a watch on several other persons too, while conversing with the lady seated beside her, and had been remarkably well-pleased with what she had observed.

'Dispensed with your many admirers at last?' she remarked as her niece resumed her seat, and smiled as violet-blue eyes were raised ceilingwards.

'It's really most flattering to be asked to stand up so often, but one can have too much of a good thing. And these dratted white slippers are nipping at my toes!'

'One would never have guessed it, my dear. You always look so graceful when on the dance-floor.'

The compliment earned her aunt a warm smile, but then Verity changed the subject by saying, 'Oh, by the by, have you seen who's here?'

'Yes, dear. I saw Major Carter arrive.'

'Is he here?' Verity glanced about the room and quickly located Brin's tall figure amongst a group of gentlemen on the opposite side of the room. 'So he is! Only I wasn't referring to him. Uncle Charles is here.'

'Yes, I know. He came in with the Major, as it happens. I didn't realise they were acquainted.'

'Er—yes. I do believe they know each other slightly,' Verity responded guardedly. It wouldn't do to let her aunt know that she had been discussing the Major with Lord Charles. It might lead to the wildest suppositions, so she quickly changed the subject. 'Who is that middle-aged gentleman talking with my uncle? I don't believe I've ever seen him before.'

'That's Lord Castleford. You danced with his nephew at the Morlands' gathering the other week, remember?'

'Ah, yes! The handsome fair-haired one. I didn't care for him very much. He thinks a great deal too much of himself. . . And there was something about him. . .' Verity shook her head as she glanced once again at the rather portly figure of Lord Castleford. 'Is his wife or son present this evening?'

'I should think it highly unlikely, dear. Neither of them cares for town life very much.'

'I have discovered someone else who's of a similar turn of mind,' Verity informed her with a slight smile. 'It would seem that little Clarissa Gillingham is more at home with the sheep and cows.'

'Really?' Lady Billington's brows rose. 'How very interesting! I wonder if that puts her out of the running?'

Verity didn't pretend to misunderstand. Almost from the day of her arrival in London she had known the identities of the three young ladies who had found favour in the dashing Major's eyes. Before today Verity had believed that little Clarissa was the most likely candidate for the position of the future Viscountess Dartwood. There was no denying that Miss Gillingham was both pretty and sweet-natured. However, what she had learned this evening had given her pause for thought.

Clarissa would only be content if she was allowed to live a simple life in the country. But would a bucolic existence suit a man who was accustomed to excitement, accustomed to facing dangers every day? It was certainly difficult to envisage. After all, that hard life out in the Peninsula, fighting for one's country, must surely have left its mark?

Verity turned her attention on the second contender, who at that precise moment was tripping lightly down the floor in an energetic dance. Hilary Fenner, of course, had known the Major longer than Verity had herself. She was a lively and very likeable girl from a good family. It was rather a pity that her tongue tended to run on wheels, and that her voice was a constant high-pitched screech. In all other respects she might have done very well, Verity mused, casting a surreptitious glance at the third candidate.

Lady Caroline Mortimer was the only daughter of the

Earl and Countess of Westbury. Verity considered her
by far the prettiest of the three, but this was marred
slightly by a rather haughty bearing. If Brin was, indeed,
serious in his attentions towards the earl's daughter then
he was aiming high. But why not? After all, the title of
Viscountess was not to be sneezed at.

'May I hope, Miss Harcourt, that you have
remembered to save me a dance?'

Verity came out of her musings with a guilty start,
and not for the first time wished that the Major could
rid himself of the unfortunate propensity he had for
miraculously appearing before her just when she
occasionally happened to be thinking about him. It really
was most unnerving!

'Of course I have, sir.' She rose to her feet, bestowing
a smile upon him that was not completely false. 'I do
believe they are about to play a waltz. How very fortunate
that I obtained permission to perform that particular
dance from the dragon-lady herself only last week.'

'For heaven's sake, child! Keep your voice down!'
Lady Billington urged in a frantic undertone, before casting a surreptitious glance at that most formidable of
patronesses, Mrs Drummond Burrell, who was seated a
mere few feet away. 'Do you want to be barred from
Almack's? Ostracised from Society?'

This drew an unmistakable wicked glint to sparkle
in the depths of violet eyes. 'Now, there's a tempting,
proposition!'

'Allow me to relieve you of your niece's rather unnerving company for a short time, ma'am,' the Major put in,
and then whisked Verity on to the dance-floor before she
could utter any further outrageous remarks to discompose
her normally imperturbable chaperon.

Verity's unholy amusement vanished the instant Brin's rather shapely, long-fingered hand touched her waist. During the past week several young gentlemen had partnered her in what many seasoned members of Society considered a most improper dance, but not one had caused her pulse rate to behave so erratically. What on earth was the matter with her? Surely it wasn't possible that in some secret, dark place deep within she had retained a *tendre* for this man? The disturbing realisation that this might well prove to be the case did little to restore her equilibrium, and she found herself having to concentrate very hard as they began to swirl about the floor lest she miss a step.

'You're very quiet.' The casual remark drew her head up, and he could quite easily discern unease of mind mirrored in the deep blue depths of her eyes. 'What's wrong?' His usual teasing tone had been replaced by one of unmistakable concern. 'What has occurred to disturb you?'

Lord, but he was astute! 'Wh-why nothing!' she assured him, but so unconvincingly that it wouldn't have fooled a halfwit. 'I'm still not at all proficient at this particular dance and should hate to step on your toes.'

'Rest easy, child. I'm sure they would survive the encounter.'

Verity was quite certain of it, too—as certain as she was that she wasn't fooling him for a moment—and she swiftly sought some change of topic. 'I understand you arrived here with Lord Charles Harcourt. Are you well acquainted with my uncle?'

'I didn't arrive here with him. We merely met on the stairs,' he volunteered, after only the slightest of pauses.

'I do know him, however. We are both members of White's.'

In that case why hadn't her uncle set himself the task of trying to discover more about the Major over a glass of port and a game of cards in the relaxing atmosphere of their club? What could have been simpler, for heaven's sake?

Verity pushed this rather puzzling thought aside and said, 'I'm rather surprised to see him here tonight. He isn't one for favouring such gatherings as this with his presence.'

'And neither is Lord Castleford, by all accounts,' Brin returned, glancing at the two gentlemen who remained conversing in one corner. 'Castleford is a close neighbour of my friend Ravenhurst, as it happens.'

Is he now? Verity's eyes narrowed fractionally. And hadn't her aunt mentioned that Castleford worked at the War Office? How very interesting!

'What a pity your friend isn't in town. I wouldn't have minded having a word with him.' She hadn't realised she had spoken her thoughts aloud until she glanced up and noticed that he was regarding her with a rather quizzical gleam in his eyes. 'About horses, you understand. After all, if he could manage to put you in the way of those greys. . .'

His expression, now, was faintly mocking. 'There isn't a snowball's chance in—There is no possibility whatsoever of his finding you a pair of horses, Miss Harcourt.'

'Oh, and why not?'

'Firstly because he isn't in favour of ladies handling the ribbons. He would never permit his own wife to tool her own carriage. And secondly because I should veto the idea. You are far too lovely to risk your neck by indulging in what I suspect would turn out to be nothing more than a passing whim.'

For a few moments it was as much as Verity could do to stop herself from giving him a well-deserved set-down for daring to suppose that he would ever be given any say in how she conducted herself, but then her sense of humour came to the fore and she found herself gurgling with laughter.

'You had the unmitigated impertinence to suggest that I was unprincipled the other day, Major Carter. I rather think that of the two of us you are the devious one. How can I possibly take you roundly to task over your lofty assumption that you could dictate how I should go on when in the next breath you pay me such a pretty compliment?'

'Spiked your guns nicely, Miss Harcourt, have I not? And to prove you bear no malice I hope you will be gracious enough to permit me to escort you in to supper later, and, of course, agree to partner me for the supper dance?'

It never crossed her mind for an instant to deny him, even though she would be breaking her golden rule of never standing up more than once with the same gentleman in any one evening. She considered their long acquaintanceship sufficient justification to disregard this excellent maxim.

Moreover, the longer she was in his company, the more likely it was that she would uncover something of importance—providing there was, in fact, something of importance to uncover.

During the following week there wasn't a day that went by when Verity was not seen in Major Carter's company,

either gliding round a dance-floor on his arm in an
evening, or seated beside him in his curricle during the
day. Society, ever watchful for the slightest nuance, was
not slow in placing its own interpretation on the sudden
preference Major Carter seemed to have acquired for
Miss Harcourt's company.

Naturally, conjecture was rife: was it possible that the
dashing Major was considering a fourth young lady as a
possible candidate for the future Viscountess Dartwood?
It certainly appeared that way. And how well they looked
together, that lovely, slender raven-haired girl and that
broad-shouldered gentleman with those striking red-
brown locks!

One would have needed to be both blind and deaf not
to have known what Society was surmising, but just what
Brin thought of the latest *on dits* was anyone's guess.
He never failed to ask her to dance if they happened to
be attending the same function of an evening, but Verity
could not in all honesty say that he singled her out for
particular attention, for if any one of the three young
ladies to whom he had been paying court since his arrival
in town happened to be present, he certainly made a point
of dancing with her, too.

For her part, Verity had at first been amused by all the
attention they drew whenever they were in each other's
company, but as the days passed she became less and
less contented, and began to experience a real sense of
guilt. She tried desperately to convince herself that her
pursuit of Brin was being made with the best possible
intentions—for the good of the country, perhaps for the
good of the man himself—but even this failed to salve
her conscience. The more she was in his company, the
more she grew to like him. She felt certain that he liked

her too. Was it fair to continue to encourage his attentions, and thereby risk his feelings for her deepening? Of course it was not! It was heartless and unjust! Furthermore, it was not worthy of her.

Things came to a head a little over a week after the Gillinghams' ball, when Verity entered the breakfast parlour to find her aunt, looking as excited as a child, already seated at the table.

'You will never guess what I have received this morning,' she gushed, her plump face wreathed in smiles. 'A letter from Sarah Ravenhurst, inviting us to stay at her country house for a few days! Here, read it for yourself.'

After casting her eyes over the short missive, written in a neat, flowing hand, Verity looked across the breakfast table with a puzzled frown creasing her brow. 'I didn't realise you were well acquainted with the Ravenhursts, Aunt Clara?'

'I'm not, dear. Naturally, I know Marcus Ravenhurst. He's rather a severe-looking, unapproachable gentleman. And I did meet his wife Sarah last year, when they came up to town for a few weeks. She really is the most lovely, charming young woman. But I'm not acquainted with either of them very well.'

'In that case, why have we been invited to Ravenhurst?'

It was as much as Lady Billington could do to stop herself from gaping across the table at her niece. The reason was patently clear to her: Sarah Ravenhurst had issued the invitation at her good friend Brin Carter's behest. So why wasn't this apparent to Verity? she wondered, reaching for the coffee-pot and filling both their cups. After all, the girl had not made the least attempt to deny the Major her company whenever he had sought it, and Lady Billington had been secretly delighted with the way things had been progressing between the two of them.

The Major, being a gentleman of superior sense, had not been over-zealous in his attentions and was, evidently, taking things very cautiously. However, it was abundantly obvious to anyone of the meanest intelligence that they enjoyed each other's company and were well suited. It was obvious, too, that Verity had put whatever childish dislike she had had of the Major firmly behind her. What wasn't so clear, though, was the depth of her feelings.

Might her niece still consider Brin Carter as nothing more than an old friend? If that was indeed the case, then it would be advisable, Lady Billington decided with rapier-like sharpness, to tread very warily lest she throw a rub in the young Major's way. But, at the same time, it would be a grave mistake to underestimate her niece's powers of perception, she decided, handing across a cup.

'From the letter I gather that Sarah Ravenhurst is inviting several people to stay. It wouldn't surprise me if Brin hasn't asked her to invite you. After all, you two appear to have become friends again. And for my part,' she went on, not offering her niece the opportunity to confirm this, 'I must say it's a great honour, and I cannot deny that I should dearly love to see that house. It is reputed to be something quite out of the common way. But we shan't decide now whether or not to accept the invitation. Let us take a day or two to think it over.'

Verity wasn't fooled for an instant. Her aunt had already made up her mind. And so, too, had she! To accept was out of the question. Unthinkable! It would be the cruellest thing imaginable to allow Brin to suppose that her affections were engaged. And how could he possibly think otherwise if she agreed to be what was tantamount to his guest at Ravenhurst? She realised with an acute feeling of guilt that she had been cruelly insensitive in her dealings with him, even though her intentions had been honourable enough. But how to set matters right? More importantly, how could she flatly refuse to accept Sarah Ravenhurst's invitation without rousing her aunt's suspicions?

Lady Billington broke into her sombre reflections by speaking of the party they were to attend that evening, and Verity forced herself to listen, but as soon as breakfast was over she took herself back upstairs and changed into her outdoor clothes. Fresh air and time by herself was the order of the day.

It was a simple matter to avoid Meg's company. Her maid never came to her room unless summoned. It wasn't so easy to avoid Horace's, however. He awaited her, as he did every morning, at the foot of the stairs, his plumed tail wagging expectantly, and Verity discovered, quite surprisingly, that she just hadn't the heart to leave him behind.

She managed to slip out of the house without being observed, but as she made her way along the street and turned the corner she couldn't rid herself of the disturbing feeling that she was being followed. She looked round on several occasions, but saw nothing and no one of a suspicious nature. There were many people abroad, and she certainly received several strange looks from members of both sexes. That, of course, was only to be expected, for it was considered grossly improper for a young lady of evident quality to be out and about on her own in the streets of London, even in broad daylight.

When at last they arrived at Green Park Verity felt a little less conspicuous. Unlike Hyde Park, it was never crowded here, and to see the herd of cows, and the milk-maids dispensing glasses of warm milk, almost made one feel one was back in the peace and quiet of the countryside.

Unfortunately, Horace took exception to sharing the park with the docile, bovine creatures. He tended to voice his displeasure rather vociferously, so Verity always kept well away from that area of park where the cows were usually to be found grazing.

After walking far enough to satisfy Horace's desire for exercise, she sat herself down on the lush grass, close to a dense area of shrubs, and began to ponder over her present, rather ticklish predicament.

A wry smile suddenly curled her lips. She had thought she had outgrown her impetuousness years ago, but apparently she most certainly had not. Since attending Miss Tinsdale's very select seminary in Bath, she had had to learn to come to terms with the many petty rules and restrictions imposed upon her sex. Women, in her opinion, were second-class citizens. They were not allowed any say in the running of their country, nor were they permitted to fight for the land of their birth.

Limitations for ladies of breeding were even more constricting. They were little more than adornments, expected only to bear children and to run a household efficiently. So was it really any wonder that she, a spirited girl of no mean intelligence, had jumped at the opportunity her uncle had offered to do something so very worthwhile? Of course it was not! But she was honest enough to admit that she had given little, if any thought to the possible consequences of her actions.

Although she had learned nothing further since the evening of the Gillinghams' ball, Verity was still certain in her own mind that Brin was no traitor to his country. But supposing she had uncovered something very much to his discredit. . .? Supposing she had discovered that he had been at the inn at Frampington on that particular Friday evening? Would she then have passed on the information to her uncle, knowing that Brin would in all likelihood have been taken into custody and possibly hanged as a traitor?

She shuddered convulsively. It didn't bear dwelling on. What she had succeeded in doing was bad enough, she reminded herself silently, experiencing a most unpleasant stabbing pain of guilt. Her willingness to be in his company had given him the totally wrong impression. She couldn't deny that she liked him. . . Yes, she liked him very well, but evidently he believed her feelings went rather deeper than mere liking. And now it was up to her to convince him otherwise without, she hoped, causing him too much pain.

'And what be tha doing out 'ere all by thissen, lass?'

Verity didn't know which of them was more startled: Horace sat bolt-upright and voiced his displeasure at the rude interruption of his pleasant doze in his usual way, and she, very nearly jumping out of her skin, inadvertently let the leash slip from her fingers. The indignant Horace wasted no time in disappearing into the shrubbery to investigate the intrusion before she could regain her hold.

'Coachman?' Verity slewed round, her eyes desperately trying to pierce the dense foliage.

'Aye, lass. . . And turn back round, tha troublesome chit! Remember what I told thee!'

Verity obeyed the brusque command without hesitation. 'Are you not in disguise? No, of course, you're not. What an incredibly foolish thing for me to have asked!' She chuckled, feeling suddenly completely at ease knowing that he was there. 'If you went about London in broad daylight dressed in mask and cloak, you would be swiftly carted off to Bow Street.'

There was no response. Even her aunt's pampered Peke had ceased his infernal yapping. 'Where's Horace?' she asked, alarmed once again.

'He's right 'ere, lass.' A short silence, then, 'I 'ope 'e ain't thy dog. Prefer bigger ones missen.'

'Of course he isn't mine! And what are you doing to him? He's very quiet.' An awful suspicion occurred to her. 'Oh, God! You haven't throttled him, have you? My aunt would never forgive me!'

'Course I've not. 'E's lying flat on 'is back wi' 'is legs in t'air in ecstasies over 'aving 'is middle tickled.'

'Well, do be careful,' she adjured him. 'He does have a tendency to bite strangers.'

'Animals don't bite me, lass. . .well, not as a rule. Only ever been attacked once in m'life. . . And that were by a vicious little cat. Don't think she'll ever try it again, mind. Not if she's got any sense, that is.'

Verity compressed her lips together primly, flatly refusing to be drawn, but when the Coachman asked again why she was about on her own, she was forced to unlock her mouth.

'I needed to be on my own, that's why!' she snapped, resenting his adopting what could best be described as a rather authoritarian tone. 'And how did you know I was here, anyway? Were you following me?'

'Aye. Often sees tha when tha's out and about. . . And tha never knows I'm there.'

'Well, there's no need for you to keep an eye on me any longer,' she told him, having by this time reached a decision. 'I've decided I shan't be helping my uncle any longer.'

There was a further short silence, then, in his customary rather rudely blunt fashion, 'And why not?'

'Because I honestly don't believe I possess the right sort of temperament for such an undertaking.'

'Come on, lass. There's more to it than that.' His tone, now, was gentle, and remained so as he added, 'What's occurred to upset thee?'

'Oh, nothing really. It's just. . .' Verity released her breath in a long sigh. 'I said right from the start that I didn't think Brin was involved, and I still don't. All I've managed to uncover during this past week is that his friend Marcus Ravenhurst had something to do with acquiring those greys. Though whether the pair belonged to Ravenhurst himself, or he merely put Brin in the way of attaining them, I don't know. Brin's as cunning as an old fox!' she went on to explain, sounding decidedly nettled. 'He neatly avoids responding to any questions he doesn't choose to answer, and, to be honest with you, I don't think I'm going to discover anything further from him.'

'Is that the only reason why tha don't wish to continue?'

'Not entirely, no. I also feel guilty.' Again she sighed. 'By willingly accepting his company so often during these past days, I rather think I've given him the totally wrong impression. . .' You see, I've been invited to Ravenhurst for a few days.'

'What of it?'

Verity raised her eyes heavenwards. Men could be so insensitive at times! 'I've never met the Ravenhursts in my life, so I can only assume the invitation was instigated by Brin himself. . .I believe he's growing—well— fond of me.'

'Bound to o' done, lass. Tha's a very lovely young woman.'

Verity couldn't help feeling inordinately pleased because he considered her so. 'Yes, well,' she responded, her cheeks growing quite pink with pleasure. 'You must see, though, that I cannot possibly accept. It would be grossly unfair. He would think his feelings were reciprocated.'

'Oh, I shouldn't worry thy pretty little head over that, if I were thee. Tha's not the only one to receive an invite. To m' certain knowledge, the earl's daughter's received one, and so too 'as that friend o' thine, the Fenner chit.'

Verity was astounded. 'How on earth can you possibly know that?'

'Makes it m' business t'know, lass. Well, 'tis common knowledge t'Major's been paying court to 'em. They received their invitations afore you.' There was a significant pause. 'Expect you were an afterthought, as tha might say.'

'An afterthought!' she echoed in a tiny squeal of indignation. Everything suddenly became crystal-clear. The wretch had invited her and the other ladies to Ravenhurst simply to vet them, to discover which of them would make the most suitable Viscountess. She had never been so insulted in her life!

'Course, it shows sound judgement, I s'pose,' the Coachman remarked fair-mindedly, breaking into her vengeful deliberations, 'iffen 'e can't quite make up 'is mind which o' you 'e prefers. Personally I don't think there's the slightest doubt. Tha's much the best. But, then, each to 'is own.'

The compliment was entirely wasted, for Verity was at that moment silently bestowing a string of far from flattering epithets on the Major as she stared sightlessly across the park.

What a fool she had been to suffer pangs of conscience over that unprincipled wretch! He really was the most callous monster to play fast and loose with ladies' feelings. Not with hers, of course. She was far too sensible to be taken in by a handsome face and an outwardly pleasing manner... Vet her, indeed! Her blood was rapidly reaching boiling point. He deserved to be taught a short, sharp lesson!

'Tha's very quiet, lass.'

'I'm thinking.'

'What about?'

'How I can wreak my revenge on that odious toad of a Major!'

A peculiar sound, like that of a suppressed chuckle, emanated from the shrubbery. 'That a girl! Go get 'im, lass! Course, it'll mean tha going to Ravenhurst.'

Her eyes narrowed to slits. 'I'm almost tempted.'

'I would, iffen I were thee. Tha never knows, tha might discover just when Ravenhurst put 'im in t'way o' those greys. And I can always find a means of contacting you when tha's there.' Leaves began to rustle. 'I must be on m' way now, lass. Can't remain skulking 'ere, otherwise folks'll think I'm up t'no good. I'll be in touch.'

The next instant Horace emerged from the shrubbery with something tucked beneath his collar. Verity removed it and a soft smile curled her lips. Why was it that whenever the Coachman was near she experienced the most wonderful feeling of security, the topsy-turvy world seeming to right itself at the sound of that husky, thickly accented voice?

She stared down at the delicate wild bloom resting in the palm of her hand. Dear Lord! Was it possible that she was in danger of losing her heart to that mysterious, sometimes infuriating man? Surely not! And yet. . .

Chapter Nine

'**E**verything I've heard about this place is true!' Lady Billington declared, totally enraptured. 'Have you ever seen anything so perfectly situated?'

Verity, staring through the post-chaise window, was forced to admit that she had not. Since their surprise invitation to Ravenhurst had become common knowledge, she had heard much of the quiet splendour of the place, and had been prepared for the incomparable sight which met her eyes as the carriage made its way down the sweeping arc of the main driveway towards the Georgian mansion. But what did come as a complete surprise was the mistress of this fine house.

Verity wasn't perfectly sure just what she had been expecting the wife of one of the richest men in the land to be like: a little haughty, perhaps, a lady who certainly knew her own worth, and one of impeccable manners, formal rather than friendly. But Sarah Ravenhurst turned out to be nothing like the lady of her imaginings, and Verity felt instantly drawn to the very pretty young matron who, not standing on ceremony, came smilingly across the hall to greet them with, 'Oh, you poor things!

141

I know the journey from London is no great distance, but it has grown so uncomfortably warm these past days and the heat this afternoon is particularly oppressive.'

'I cannot deny it is a relief to be out of that stuffy post-chaise,' Lady Billington responded with feeling. 'My niece and I decided to hire a carriage. You must have more than enough to cope with finding room for personal maids without the added burden of so many coachmen and grooms, not to mention horses.'

'That was very thoughtful of you both. Lady Gillingham was equally considerate.' There was a decided twinkle in Sarah Ravenhurst's eyes. 'We do have a more than adequate coach-house, but I'm afraid the Countess's travelling carriage is rather on the large size and takes up a good deal of space.'

'Never tell me she travelled here in that ancient landau!' Lady Billington's pained expression betrayed quite beautifully her staunch disapproval. 'The Dowager Countess had it specially made. Why, you could fit a bed inside!'

'My aunt is a fount of wisdom, Mrs Ravenhurst. There isn't much that occurs in Society as a whole which escapes her notice,' Verity remarked wryly, drawing their hostess's eyes on her, and just for a moment she thought she could detect an arresting look in their lovely aquamarine depths, but in the next instant it was gone.

'I am not many years your senior, Miss Harcourt, so I do not think we need stand on ceremony. I hope you will call me Sarah and permit me to call you Verity. Such a pretty name, I've always thought.'

Then, without giving her young guest time to acquiesce or not, she led the way up the beautifully carved wooden staircase, explaining as she did so that they would be dining quite informally that evening, and that it was destined to be an all-female occasion as Brin was not due to arrive until much later and her husband had, unfortunately, been called away on business. This latter snippet of information drew a rather wicked smile to curl Verity's lips, but as their hostess was at that precise moment showing Lady Billington into her allotted bedchamber it went completely undetected, and by the time Sarah had turned to lead the way out of the room Verity had managed to school her features.

'I've put you in here.' Sarah opened the very next door along the passageway. 'I thought you would like to be near your aunt.'

Verity found herself standing in a bright, airy bedchamber, decorated quite charmingly in varying shades of blue. 'Oh, how lovely! Blue is my favourite colour.'

'Yes, exceedingly pretty,' Sarah agreed, staring fixedly at her young guest's delicately featured face. 'I expect like the others you are tired after the journey, so I shall leave you to rest before dinner.'

'I'm not such a poor creature. But if you're busy, please do not let me detain you.'

'On the contrary, I should be more than happy to stay for a while. It will give us the opportunity to become acquainted.' After making herself comfortable in the window embrasure, Sarah watched Verity untie the ribbons of her very fetching bonnet. She knew a little of her other young visitors, but where Verity was concerned Brin had not been very forthcoming, and she couldn't help wondering what lay behind his reticence. 'Am I right in thinking you have known Brin for quite some time?'

'Yes. I was not much above ten years old the first time we met. My mother returned to her native Yorkshire shortly after my father died. Sadly, she outlived him by only two years, and I continued to live with Uncle Lucius, my guardian.' Verity's lips curled into a tender smile as she joined Sarah on the window seat. 'He's a dear man. We get along together famously.'

'In which case you are to be envied, my dear. My guardian was a most unpleasant individual. Quite loathsome, in fact!' There was a decidedly wicked little smile playing about Sarah's lips. 'But he has made quite a remarkably wonderful husband. I could not have found a better man for the role.'

'Ravenhurst was your guardian?' Verity clapped her hands together in delight. 'Here's a lively tale! Oh, do tell me everything!'

It had been Sarah's intention to learn as much as she could about this vibrant young woman, but she found herself relating a little of her own life history: of how, three years before, she had taken it upon herself to leave Bath; of how Ravenhurst, in hot pursuit, had run her to earth at a wayside inn where a murder had subsequently been committed.

Verity listened with rapt interest, her lovely eyes bright with excitement. 'How very enlivening! And very romantic too, of course, your falling in love and marrying your guardian. It's a great pity he isn't here. I would very much have liked to make his acquaintance.'

'He'll be returning in plenty of time for the party on Friday,' Sarah assured her. 'It was—er—most unfortunate that he was called away at such a time.'

'Wasn't it just!' Verity agreed, but was unable to control a quivering lip, and Sarah, her lively sense of humour never far from the surface, dissolved into laughter.

'Oh, I can see it's a complete waste of time trying to

fool you. Yes, the wretch has left me to my own devices,' she admitted. 'I'm afraid Marcus can be a little intolerant at times, most especially with certain members of our sex. All in all, it was perhaps for the best that he did decide to make himself scarce.'

'In which case he has been more than generous in opening his doors to a passel of females, most of whom I'm certain are completely unknown to him,' Verity responded fair-mindedly, before the glinting amusement in her own eyes began to fade. 'Which is more than can be said for Major Carter. His manners leave much to be desired, it would seem. Not only does he trade on your evident close friendship by persuading you to invite certain persons to your home, but he hasn't the common courtesy to lend you his support when his guests arrive.'

Sarah could not detect so much as a trace of resentment, or even pique in the pleasant voice, only cool detachment, which she found infinitely more disturbing, and she hurriedly came to her friend's defence.

'Brin did warn me that he wouldn't be here until the evening, Verity. And please do not imagine that I was coerced into opening my home, because I tell you plainly I was not. Nothing could have pleased me more.'

She turned her head to stare out of the window at the acres of rolling parkland. 'I love Ravenhurst and am more than content to spend most of the year here. I'm afraid Marcus and I are considered a very odd couple. Quite old-fashioned, in fact! We very much enjoy each other's company. Since our marriage, three years ago, I have borne him two children and have only ever spent two very short spells in London. I'm afraid I'm in the gravest danger of becoming quite anti-social. So you see,' she went on, transferring her gaze to Verity's delicate features, 'when Brin offered me the opportunity to play the hostess to such a fashionable gathering of young ladies, I virtually jumped at the chance. My only fear is that you will swiftly become bored with the simple country pastimes after the sophisticated entertainments of the Season.'

Verity didn't doubt her hostess's sincerity, and was surprised to find her annoyance rapidly fading. 'I can safely promise you that I most certainly shall not. Like yourself, I much prefer the country. Believe me, your invitation to escape the capital and the endless social gatherings for a few days was a godsend!'

This assertion seemed to afford Sarah a great deal of satisfaction, and she continued to converse so openly on those subjects dearest to her heart that by the time she left the room a short while later Verity was in no doubt that the delightful Mrs Ravenhurst was touchingly devoted to Brin.

It was fair to assume that Sarah knew precisely why Brin had asked her to invite certain persons to her home, but whether she approved his motives was quite a different matter. It was evident, too, that Sarah was very much in love with her husband; had fallen in love with him soon after they had met. Therefore it was not inconceivable that she would wish the man she looked upon almost as a brother to attain the same marital bliss; that she would want Brin to be in love with the woman he eventually married.

A wry smile curled Verity's lips. Poor Sarah was doomed to disappointment, she feared. How on earth could Brin's affections be engaged when he was still considering one of four possible candidates for his future Viscountess?

Like four brood mares, Clarissa, Hilary, Lady Caroline and—curse it!—even she herself had been invited to Ravenhurst to parade for his thorough inspection. A gurgle of laughter escaped her as she moved across to the bell-pull to summon Meg. Up until her arrival her proud Harcourt blood had coursed through her veins, hotly demanding retribution on the man who had dared to suppose that she might vie for his attention and approval, but meeting Sarah Ravenhurst had had a surprisingly soothing effect upon her and, strangely, she no longer craved revenge.

The wretch still deserved to be taught a short, sharp lesson, and if the opportunity arose she doubted she would be able to resist the temptation to mete out some much needed punishment, but she had no intention, now, of going out of her way to be difficult or to cause Brin embarrassement, as she had once fully intended to do.

No, she would merely sit back and no doubt derive much amusement from the spectacle of seeing the other three young ladies being put through their paces while, at the same time, she became better acquainted with the charming Mrs Ravenhurst.

During dinner that evening Verity was given ample opportunity to study their hostess more closely. If Sarah believed she was in danger of becoming anti-social, then she betrayed no sign of it. Her manners were faultless, she was both gracious and friendly, and what Verity particularly liked was the way Sarah treated everyone equally: bestowing no undue deference towards the Countess of Westbury, who undoubtedly possessed the highest social standing.

She was also given the opportunity to study more

closely the contenders for the position of Viscountess Dartwood.

Clarissa, who seemed remarkably cheerful, possibly because she was in the country again, continued to remain her firm favourite for the title. She was a kind-hearted, unassuming girl who would make any man a very comfortable wife.

There was no denying that Hilary Fenner, too, was a good-natured female. Although Hilary wasn't a particularly close friend, Verity had always got on very well with her. It was her propensity to chatter, however, which might prove to be her undoing, a fault which could never be levelled at the Countess's daughter.

Apart from the occasional 'yes' or 'no', when addressed directly, Lady Caroline barely uttered a word, and yet it was she who very nearly proved to be Verity's undoing when, in response to Sarah's suggestion that the ladies might like to visit a place of interest in the morning, she raised her eyes from the food on her plate and said imperiously, 'We shall go to Oxford!'

Verity's eyes, glinting with unholy amusement, met those of her equally diverted hostess across the table, and it was left to the imperturbable Lady Gillingham to break the ensuing silence.

'I think that a capital notion! I have never been there and would very much like to pay a visit.'

With the exception of Verity, who dared not speak lest she betray her mirth, and the Countess, who said she would forgo the pleasure as she was not a particularly good traveller in warm weather, all the other guests voiced their whole-hearted approval to the trip, and so Sarah offered to put her open carriage at their disposal.

'But we cannot all possibly fit into just the one carriage,' Hilary pointed out after her mother had thanked their hostess for the kind offer.

'We can take our carriage as well, dear,' Mrs Fenner suggested, but Hilary was far from satisfied with that.

'It won't be as pleasant as riding in the open air.'

'I shall not be accompanying you,' Sarah informed them. 'I shall remain here with Lady Westbury.'

'And I, too, shall forgo this trip,' Verity announced, drawing a rather concerned look from her aunt.

'Why? You do not feel unwell, I trust?'

'No, Aunt Clara. As hale and hearty as ever. It's just that I have a fancy to explore these beautiful grounds here.'

'Well, that still leaves six of us,' Hilary reminded them, her peevish tone making it abundantly clear to everyone that she didn't relish the prospect of being one of those forced to travel in a closed carriage, and drew an understanding smile from her hostess.

'I'm sure Brin would be only too delighted to act as your escort,' Sarah said. 'He will probably wish to take his curricle, so one of you young ladies could travel with him.'

'I shall go in the curricle!'

Once again Lady Caroline's majestic utterance brought a glow of wicked amusement to Verity's eyes, which brightened considerably when she caught the malevolent glance that Hilary cast the imperious earl's daughter.

All in all, she mused, the next few days were so fair to affording her untold amusement. There was every chance that Hilary would come to cuffs with Lady Caroline long before the visit was over, and it would be interesting to see if the unobtrusive little Clarissa managed to gain her fair share of the gallant Major's attention.

Most interesting of all would be to view her hostess's reaction to the events of the next few days, for unless she was very much mistaken, and she didn't think she was, Sarah Ravenhurst had a rather wicked sense of humour, not unlike her own.

Verity's delight at the prospect of an amusing sojourn in the country received an unexpected and rather severe knock as soon as the ladies rose from the table. They were invited to repair to the drawing-room, where a gold-painted instrument of majestic proportions had been placed near the pianoforte in one corner of the room. Sarah's suggestion that one of the ladies might like to entertain them was instantly taken up by Lady Caroline who, in her now all-too-familiar commanding way, said, 'I shall play!'

She proved to be a rather gifted player, and Verity was not slow in adding her voice to the general praises when the earl's daughter had come to the end of her lively little piece. Hilary, not to be outdone, didn't hesitate to take up the position on the stool, and she, too, performed very creditably, but when Clarissa was then invited to display her skill on the harp, Verity decided that it was time she made a quick exit.

As luck would have it her chair was placed near the long French window, which had been left open to allow a little fresh air into the room. She waited only until all eyes were focused on Clarissa's dainty fingers plucking at the strings and then slipped outside, undetected, she hoped, and sped along the path, only to collide with a large, immovable object as she rounded the corner. Strong hands gripped her upper arms, steadying her, and she found herself staring up at the golden flecks in Major Carter's twinkling brown eyes.

'Here, let me pass!' she demanded, after ineffectually struggling to free herself from his hold. 'Besides which, your presence is required inside.'

One russet brow rose mockingly. 'And yours isn't, I suppose?'

'Not at the moment, no.'

He caught the faint strains of music and betrayed his immediate understanding by a twitching smile. 'Evidently you are not a young lady who appreciates the finer arts.'

'Not that infernal twanging, I don't!' Verity retorted, not mincing words, then found herself responding to that smile. 'Now, be a gentleman, Brin, and allow me to pass before that wretched aunt of mine comes in search of me.'

'Oh, so it's Brin again, is it? he remarked, sublimely disregarding her request. 'Since our first meeting in London I have been forced to contend with a very formal *Major Carter*, and during the past few days a frigidly spoken *sir*. So I can only assume that whatever I did to annoy you—though heaven knows what it was!—has been forgiven and forgotten.'

He watched a decidedly guarded look replace the flicker of amusement in her eyes and prudently changed the subject. 'Well, I take it you've dined already. Sarah does tend to keep country hours here at Ravenhurst. Did you have a good journey? When did you arrive?'

Her expression changed instantly now that she was on safer ground. 'Several hours ago. And we were on time. Which is more than can be said for you!'

'Disappointed I wasn't here to greet you, lass?'

She looked at him sharply. Never before had she heard him use any Yorkshire term, and there was something vaguely familiar in the tone. 'I've never heard you resort to any Yorkshire expression before.'

'I do from time to time,' he admitted, at last releasing his hold, and Verity took immediate advantage by stepping back a pace. 'The men in my regiment used to find it amusing. My estimable grandparent certainly didn't, mind,' he went on, his smile turning rueful. 'Many a skelping I got when I was a lad when he caught me talking broad Yorkshire. I was born the son of a gentleman, and had to speak like a gentleman.'

Verity recalled Arthur Brinley referring to his grandson on numerous occasions as 'quality made', and her eyes softened in memory, but only for a moment.

'Evidently he didn't beat you hard enough as you continue to fall back into your old ways.'

Surprisingly he made no attempt to respond to her gentle teasing, and after a few moments she raised her eyes from the folds of his intricately tied neckcloth to look into his face, and then instantly wished she hadn't. There was such a strange look in the tawny depths of his eyes, a mixture of warm appreciation and something else—something so disturbing in its intensity that she felt the muscles of her abdomen tighten suddenly.

'You—you had better go inside and present yourself, Major Brin Carter,' she forced from a suddenly dry throat. 'The ladies await the pleasure of your company.'

'May I not escort you back inside? I'm certain the young lady has completed her rendition.'

'Thank you, no. I think I'll take a wander in the garden for a short while.' She didn't add that she needed time to pull herself together. Really, she was behaving like some lovesick schoolgirl! And there was absolutely no reason for it, either! she chided silently. She had over-

come her infatuation for this man years ago. . .
Hadn't she?

She turned and walked slowly away without another
word, but instinctively knew he was watching her and
forced herself to control the rather childish desire to run.
Only when she had turned the corner, out of sight of that
disturbing gaze, did she allow herself to relax but even
so she couldn't resist looking over her shoulder just to
ensure that he wasn't following.

Arriving at the end of the path which ran the whole
length of the moderately sized mansion, Verity found
herself in the stable yard. A middle-aged, stockily-built
groom was in the process of leading Brin's horses into
the large stone-built stable block, talking softly to them
as he encouraged the spirited pair through the doorway.

Without conscious thought she crossed what had to be
the cleanest cobbled yard she had ever seen and entered
the stable to discover a row of fine animals, each in its
own roomy stall, some contentedly chomping away on
sweet-smelling hay, whilst others stood with their heads
over the doors, watching with evident rapt interest the
settlement of the new arrivals.

'Evening, miss. And a very fine evening it be too.'

'Yes, indeed.' Verity's lips curled into a glowing
smile, which many an experienced male had found irresistible, as she moved towards the friendly groom who
was busily rubbing down one of Brin's greys. 'Lovely
animals, are they not?'

'They are that, miss. Couldn't choose between these
and the master's pair, yonder.' He gestured towards the
end two stalls and Verity turned her head to run her eyes
over the other two greys. 'My master knows a thing
or two about 'orseflesh, miss.' His brawny shoulders

shook. 'Still, he ought to. Taught 'im m'self!'

Verity had made up her mind to have nothing further
to do with her uncle Charles's very serious investigations.
She had felt a traitor herself when she had informed
him, two days before, that she simply couldn't continue
working on his behalf. She would have given almost
anything to do some small service for her country, and
she still would, but she was sensible enough to realise
that she just simply didn't possess the right sort of temperament to inform on people whom she liked. So it quite
astounded her when she found herself remarking. 'Ah,
yes! I recall Major Carter saying that Mr Ravenhurst is
an excellent judge of horseflesh. He put Brin in the way
of this pair, I understand?'

'Aye, miss. That 'e did.'

Let it go, Verity! Don't continue or you might regret
it, the voice of conscience warned, but that strong desire
to be of use to King and Country persisted like some
irritating itch.

'I'm surprised he could have brought himself to part
with such magnificent beasts.'

'Oh, they didn't belong to the master, Miss Harcourt.'

Thank heavens for that! Verity raised her eyes in silent
gratitude to the Almighty for having spared her the agony
of deciding whether or not to inform on Marcus
Ravenhurst. Now that she knew for sure that her kindly
hostess's husband was innocent of any traitorous dealings, ought she to try to discover more?

She was still debating within herself when a thought
suddenly struck her. 'How do you know my name?'

'Major Brin told me.' There was a definite twitching
at the corners of the groom's thin-lipped mouth. "Sutton,"
says 'e, "if you sees a little lady with the deepest of deep

blue eyes, and hair like a raven's wing, that'll be Miss Harcourt, and you can safely saddle up a beast of spirit for her iffen she's inclined to ride. A capital little 'orse-woman is Miss Harcourt," says 'e.'

Damned impudence! Verity thought, not flattered in the least. And just how Brin could possibly know what kind of horsewoman she was defeated her completely, since he had not seen her in the saddle for a very long time, and in those bygone days she had been forced to ride a very docile pony.

'How very considerate of him to apprise you of my ability,' she forced out between gritted teeth before swallowing her ire. 'I should very much like to put one of your master's beasts through its paces.'

She fixed her attention upon Brin's greys once more. 'One does not come across such fine animals very often. Do you happen to know how your master managed to put the Major in the way of these beauties, Sutton?'

If he considered the question more than unusually inquisitive he betrayed no signs of it. 'I do that, miss. They come from the Castleford estate. Their lands border with the master's to the north.'

Castleford, Verity echoed silently. Now *that* snippet of information she was prepared to pass on to Lord Charles. He would no doubt find it most interesting.

'I had better be getting back inside, otherwise your mistress will think I've got myself lost. It has been a pleasure making your acquaintance, Sutton,' she told him, with such a radiant smile that he was afterwards overheard to remark that Miss Harcourt had the sweetest smile, barring the mistress's, he had ever seen, and that it was enough to melt the hardest man's heart.

Verity, little realising the effect she had had upon the

Ravenhursts' head groom, made her way along the path to the front entrance and was admitted by Stebbings, who promptly handed her a letter.

'It was discovered pushed under the door, Miss Harcourt,' he explained in response to her rather puzzled glance at her name written in a bold and unfamiliar hand. 'It was Major Carter who noticed it when I admitted him a short while ago.'

After thanking the butler, Verity didn't waste a moment in having her curiosity satisfied. Rushing up the stairs to the privacy of her room, she broke the seal to read

Darling lass,

I am nearby, as promised. If you need to contact me for any reason then go to The Three Swans at Houghton. There, ask for Thomas Stone, and he will pass on any message.

Your Coachman.

Instinctively, Verity's lips curled into yet another of those devastating smiles. Was he in truth *her* Coachman? More importantly, did she want him to be hers?

Since the evening of the Morlands' party he had, increasingly, intruded into her thoughts, and not always favourably. No one could ever have accused her of having a romantic disposition, and yet the memory of his kisses, of that hard, muscular body pressed against her own, never failed to arouse the most ardent need deep inside.

Her smile slowly began to fade and she shook her head in disbelief at her own folly. It was madness, unutterable madness to feel as she did! she told herself roundly. What did she know about him, after all? She cast her eyes once again over the few boldly written lines, conjuring up an image of that tall, mysterious figure as she did so.

He was certainly an intelligent and educated man for all that he spoke with a broad Yorkshire accent, but that, she suspected, was put on for her benefit, for there had been numerous occasions when his accent had been far from pure. That little subterfuge apart, she didn't doubt his loyalty and trustworthiness were beyond question, otherwise Lord Charles would never have chosen him for such a vitally important task. And strangely enough she trusted him too; had done so right from the first time he had kissed her in that stable. She had instinctively known that he would never really harm her.

Yet was this sufficient reason to contemplate spending the rest of her life at his side? No, of course it was not! It was foolish beyond measure even to think of marriage until she had come to know him a good deal better. It was only a feather-brained female who would ever allow her heart to rule her head!

Reaching for the book of poems that she had brought with her from London, Verity placed the letter behind the delicate wild flower which she had so carefully pressed between the book's covers, and smiled crookedly at her own folly.

'I think,' she murmured, 'yes, I rather think I'm in the gravest danger of becoming quite feather-brained.'

Chapter Ten

Following instructions to the letter, Perkins entered his master's bedchamber early the next morning to discover the Major, already dressed in shirt and breeches, seated at the dressing table.

He had been the Major's valet a few short weeks only, and thought that he couldn't have been blessed with a more thoughtful or less exacting master. Not once had he seen him out of temper, although the Major sometimes seemed abstracted, as though he had a great deal on his mind. This morning, however, there were no traces of worry as his master paused in his whistling of a lively ditty to bid a cheerful greeting.

'And a very pleasant morning it is too, sir,' Perkins responded, handing the Major one expertly starched cravat before laying the others he carried very carefully in one of the drawers.

'Anyone up and about, Perkins?' Brin asked as he began to twist the long length of linen skilfully round his neck.

'I believe the mistress is in the breakfast parlour, sir.'

Brin couldn't prevent a smile at this innocent slip of

the tongue. Perkins had been employed as footman in the Ravenhurst household for a number of years before becoming his valet, a change of situation which Sarah herself had suggested when she had learned that Brin had sold his commission in the army and would be living for a time in the capital.

'You cannot possibly continue to dress yourself, Brin,' she had told him with that teasing smile of hers. 'It simply isn't done! And as I cannot imagine your putting up with such a pernickety person as Marcus's valet, I suggest you ask Perkins to be your personal manservant. I know he wishes to improve himself. He's meticulous in carrying out his duties, but young enough for you to train him to your particular requirements. I think he's wasted as a footman. He would make an excellent valet.'

'It might have escaped your notice, Perkins, but I don't happen to be married. You do not have a mistress. . .yet.'

The young man coloured to the roots of his sandy-fair hair. 'I do beg your pardon, sir.'

'Don't fret yourself, lad. It doesn't worry mè none. Although,' he went on with a decided gleam in his eyes, 'I doubt your former master would be any too pleased if he overheard you referring to his wife as my mistress.'

'Sir, I never meant. . .I would never dream of suggesting. . .' He ceased his somewhat disjointed explanations when he realised he was being teased and his lips curled into a rather boyish half-smile. 'Quite so, sir!'

'Glad to see you can take a joke, Perkins,' Brin remarked approvingly. 'Do you happen to know if Mrs Ravenhurst is alone?'

'One of the young ladies has already left her room, sir. I passed her on the stairs a few minutes ago.'

'Which one?'

'I'm afraid I'm not familiar with their names, sir.'

'Describe her.'

'She was very pretty,' Perkins responded, the embarrassed hue returning to his cheeks.

'That doesn't help much, lad. They're all pretty.'

'Not like this one, sir,' Perkins so far forgot himself to remark. 'She has black hair and the loveliest deep blue eyes I've ever—'

'Say no more!' Brin, satisfied with the folds in his cravat, rose from the dressing-table. 'The blue superfine, Perkins, I think.'

He slipped his arms into the impeccably cut jacket, and then wasted no further time in joining Sarah and Verity in the breakfast parlour. He received a charming smile from one and a mere nod from the other in response to his cheerful greeting, before seating himself down beside his hostess.

'I don't believe our young guest is in the best of humours this morning, Sarah,' he remarked provocatively while helping himself to several slices of ham. 'I cannot recall her being moody as a child. Headstrong, yes, but not prone to fits of the sullens. But then—' he shrugged '—people do change as they get older, I suppose.'

'Pity you haven't,' came the muttered response from across the table, drawing a chuckle from both Brin and the lady of the house.

'I can see that you two do not stand upon ceremony. Which is no bad thing. But for your information, Brin, Verity isn't suffering from a fit of "the sullens", as you phrase it. We were having a very comfortable coze before you came in.'

One russet-coloured brow rose. 'About me, was it?'

'What on earth makes you suppose that we'd wish to start the day by discussing such a mundane topic?' Verity interposed before Sarah could reply.

She was far from being in an offhand mood, even though she suspected that he was doing his level best to provoke her. But why must he come down to breakfast looking so damnably attractive? The mere sight of him was enough to send any young female's heart fluttering. But she was determined that he would never discover the effect he still had upon her, and if to achieve her objective meant that she must appear slightly churlish... then so be it!

'As a matter of fact, before you came in, Sarah very kindly offered to show me round this beautiful house of hers, once she's seen you all safely on your way to Oxford, that is.'

Reaching for her coffee-cup, Verity didn't see his expression change suddenly, but Sarah most certainly noticed his smile fade and a slight frown momentarily crease his brow.

'Verity decided yesterday evening that she would forgo the trip as she preferred to explore Ravenhurst. And please feel free to ride whenever you wish,' she went on, looking back at the young woman who was beginning to intrigue her more and more with every passing minute. 'Just send a message to the stables and Sutton will ensure that a suitable mount is saddled for you. In fact, I would be grateful if you exercised my mare whilst you're here. I do not take her out nearly as often as I ought.'

'I should love to, Sarah. Unfortunately I omitted to bring my habit.'

'That isn't a problem. I have several and we're much

the same size. You're more than welcome to borrow one of mine.'

'You shouldn't encourage her, Sarah,' Brin advised, not offering Verity the chance to voice her sincere thanks. 'She always did have a propensity for going off on her own. She'll only end by getting herself lost and you'll be forced to order every able-bodied man on the place out searching for her.'

Verity kept her eyes lowered, suddenly finding the crusts on her plate of immense interest. She would have been the first to admit that, as a child, she had been known on occasions to go off on her own, but she had never ridden very far, nor had she ever caused either her mother or her guardian concern over her welfare by remaining away from home for any great length of time.

Since leaving the seminary, almost five years ago, she had always adhered, except on that recent occasion when she had made that unforgettable but fruitless trip to Little Frampington, to her guardian's request that she take a groom with her whenever she went riding. Consequently, she considered Brin's remarks not only completely unwarranted, but grossly unfair, and she suspected that he knew they were too.

She was now firmly convinced that he was deliberately trying to annoy her. The only possible reason for his wishing to do so that occurred to her was because he was still nettled over her behaviour towards him the previous evening.

When she had eventually returned to the salon to rejoin the other ladies, it had been to discover that Brin was already there. It had quite sickened Verity to see how the three contenders for the title of Viscountess Dartwood had made such an inordinate fuss of him, clinging to

his every word and giggling at his remarks like three
simpletons. Steadfastly refusing to join the little group
of admirers, Verity had seated herself on the couch with
Mrs Fenner and Lady Gillingham and when, a few
minutes later, Brin had crossed the room, heading in their
direction, she had quite pointedly risen from the couch
and had gone to seat herself beside their hostess.

Raising her eyes, she risked a quick glance across the
table at him. The quizzical glint in his eyes confirmed
her suspicion, and only her resolve not to cause their
kindly hostess embarrassment prevented Verity from
yielding to his deliberate provocation and retaliating with
a few well-chosen words. She was very well aware,
though, that her tolerance level was not always high, and
quickly made an excuse to leave the table before the
temptation to toss the dregs of her coffee-cup in Brin's
direction became too strong!

Sarah was under no illusions, either, that her good
friend had gone out of his way to be deliberately aggra-
vating. Now, had it been her husband sitting beside her
at the table, she certainly wouldn't have been in the least
surprised to hear him passing some provocative remark.
He was renowned for doing just that—adorable wretch
that he was! But she had never known Brin try to put
anyone out of countenance before. So why should he
have behaved in such an uncharacteristic fashion towards
Verity? It really was most intriguing!

But by the time she had risen from the breakfast table,
having had leisure to witness Brin's attitude towards the
other young ladies, all of whom entered the room shortly
after Venty's departure, she was no longer groping in
the dark for a possible reason for her friend's rather
puzzling behaviour.

The instant the girls had joined them at the table Brin had returned to his usual urbane self. He had listened to Hilary's prattle with an indulgent ear, had quickly put the shy and sweet-natured Clarissa at her ease and had even managed to extract a reasonable amount of conversation from the normally taciturn Lady Caroline. In all honesty Sarah couldn't have said that he had betrayed a preference for any one of them, but instinct told her that he favoured Clarissa. But even Lady Gillingham's charming daughter had failed to ignite that certain something that Sarah had glimpsed for one unguarded moment when his eyes had rested upon Verity.

It would certainly be most interesting to see how things developed between those two in the next couple of days, Sarah mused, mounting the stairs to make her first visit of the day to the nursery. If Brin was serious in his intentions, and she was firmly convinced now that he was, and that this little interlude in the country was not the complete and utter sham she had once suspected it might be, he was certainly going about fixing his interests in a most peculiar way. Surely it made more sense to charm the girl, to pay her pretty compliments and be attentive to her every need? So why had he gone out of his way to make her hackles rise? She shook her head in puzzlement. Men did go about things in the oddest ways sometimes. Although, she supposed, they must have their reasons.

And what of the girl herself? A slight frown marred the perfection of Sarah's forehead. Verity's feelings were somewhat harder to define. There was no denying that she had made a point of keeping him at a distance the previous evening. There was no denying, either, that she seemed a completely different person when in Brin's company: coolly aloof, watchful almost. On the surface it appeared that she wasn't very fond of him at all, and yet Sarah sensed that this was far from the truth. It was almost as if Verity had built up a protective wall about herself to keep Brin firmly at bay. But if he succeeded in breaking down that barrier, by whatever method he chose, then what would be the outcome?

Sarah's smile returned. Yes, it would be most interesting to watch developments during the next few days; not interfere, of course, merely observe, and see how successful Brin was in storming the citadel!

Later that morning Verity, sublimely unaware that her every word, her every gesture was being studied with intense interest by the lady of the house, accompanied her aunt outside to the open carriage awaiting to take the ladies on their outing to Oxford.

Mrs Fenner had unfortunately succumbed to a sick headache and had decided to forgo the trip. Which meant, of course, that there was now ample room in the carriage to accommodate all the ladies. Lady Caroline was already seated in Brin's curricle, and no one attempted, or perhaps dared, to suggest that she ride in the open carriage with the others.

'Are you certain you won't change your mind and join us, dear?' Lady Billington asked as she seated herself beside Hilary. 'I'm certain you'd enjoy the outing.'

'I'm sure I would too,' Verity agreed, 'but I would prefer to stay here and explore the grounds.'

'You won't be able to avoid me indefinitely,' Brin's wickedly taunting voice whispered in her ear, making Verity start visibly.

She flashed him a darkling look. 'Go away!' she

breathed, not mincing words, and then louder, 'The ladies await your pleasure, Major.'

Sarah, standing a few feet away, didn't hear the little interchange, but she couldn't mistake the look of irritation on Verity's face. Evidently Brin was persisting, with provocation as his main weapon.

'If I were you, Brin, I'd take the ladies to The Bell for luncheon,' she suggested, stepping forward a pace or two. 'One can always be assured of excellent fare.'

'Yes, and please don't feel obliged to hurry over your meal.' Verity's smile was a study in roguishness. 'Remember we ladies do not enjoy gobbling down our food.'

'Believe me, I shall ensure all return none the worse for their trip. And,' he added, once again placing his lips close to her ear, 'believe me, I shall ensure that I see you later, too.'

'Not if I see you first, you won't!' she countered, completely unmoved by the challenging edge to his voice.

He looked as though he was about to say something further, but then seemed to think better of it and, after exchanging a few words of farewell with Sarah, climbed into his curricle.

As soon as Brin had given his greys the office to start and led the way up the sweep of the drive, Verity released her breath in an unmistakable sigh of relief, and then turned to discover her hostess regarding her with a not unpleasant, but quite unreadable look in her eyes.

'Are you sure you can spare the time to show me round this fine house of yours, Sarah? I'm not such a poor creature that I cannot find something to occupy me until the sightseers return. And you do now have

Mrs Fenner as well as the Countess to consider.'

'Of course I'm not too busy. I shall enjoy your company,' Sarah assured her, entwining her arm through Verity's in a sisterly way and leading her back into the spacious hall. 'The servants see to most everything. And as far as my other two guests are concerned. . . Lady Westbury, it seems, is more than content to pass the morning plying her needle, and Mrs Fenner assures me that a few hours in bed, with the curtains drawn across the window, is usually enough to rid her of her troublesome malady. So for the remainder of the morning, certainly, I'm more than happy to bear you company.'

In view of this charming assurance Verity suffered no pangs of conscience as she spent the next couple of hours leisurely inspecting most of the rooms in the house, which managed superbly to combine both elegance and comfort. A quick visit to the nursery offered her the opportunity to meet Hugo Ravenhurst, the boisterous two-year-old who already betrayed definite signs of having inherited his father's famous scowl, and of viewing the latest addition to the family who was sound asleep in her cot. The tour ended in the library, the master's inner sanctum, a room which seemed to exude its owner's personality: solid, dependable and infinitely masculine.

The instant they entered, Verity's nostrils were assailed by an unmistakable mixture of smells: leather, brandy and tobacco. Seemingly Sarah could detect the faint odour of cheroots, too, for she went straight over to the window.

'Brin's been in here this morning,' she remarked, wrinkling up her nose as she threw one of the windows wide to let in some fresh air. 'I'm afraid he picked up the habit of smoking whilst out in the Peninsula, and

Marcus allows him to indulge his vice in here.'

Verity had been listening with only half an ear, for her attention was drawn to the painting of the master and mistress above the fireplace. She couldn't prevent a slight smile as she recalled the picture of Marcus Ravenhurst in the long gallery, painted, she guessed, several years ago, but in this likeness his features seemed far less harsh, and although he wasn't smiling precisely, he looked a man who was more than just a little contented with life.

'I think you've mellowed your husband, Sarah,' she remarked.

'It's a very good likeness.' The love she bore him was mirrored in her eyes. 'Yes, he has changed during these past few years,' she admitted. 'He's far more tolerant than he used to be, but I cannot take all the credit for that. His friendship with Brin means an awful lot to him. Why, they are more like brothers!'

'Which is rather strange in itself when one considers that they haven't been acquainted for any great number of years. Although. . .' Verity looked thoughtfully into space '. . .I suppose there are those who instinctively take to each other. And there was that time Brin was convalescing here after the injuries he sustained at Badajoz.'

'You know about that. . .? Of course, Brin must have told you. How very foolish of me!'

'No, Brin didn't tell me. . . You did.' Verity gurgled with laughter at the look of astonished disbelief on her hostess's pretty face. 'Yes, Sarah,' she reiterated, 'in a way it was you who told me. You wrote to Brin's grandfather on several occasions, informing him of his grandson's progress. As you probably remember, Arthur Brinley was unwell himself, too ill to make the journey to Oxfordshire. What you probably didn't know was that his eyesight was failing fast. I visited him most every day. I read your letters to him, and it was I who penned the ones he dictated in response.'

'Good heavens!' Sarah was startled and appeared more than a little confused. 'And all this time Brin has believed. . .' Her words faded as the door opened and the butler entered to inform his mistress that luncheon was now ready and that Lady Westbury and Mrs Fenner were at the present moment making their way to the dining-room.

Sarah and Verity didn't waste any time joining them. It was a relief to discover that Mrs Fenner had fully recovered from her headache, and as the Countess proved she was far more adept at the gentle art of conversation than her daughter appeared to be the meal passed very pleasantly.

Directly afterwards they all retired to the small parlour, where the conversation tended to revolve around the efficient running of a large household. Verity could summon up little enthusiasm for a topic she knew next to nothing about and found herself with increasing frequency staring out of the window at the glorious parkland sweeping away from the house in a gentle upward slope. The day was warm and dry and the countryside beckoned, so, as soon as she felt she could excuse herself without appearing rude, she slipped upstairs to collect her bonnet and parasol and to don a pair of stout calf-boots, and then wasted not another moment in venturing out of doors.

Having given little thought to viewing any particular feature of the park, Verity merely set off in a northerly direction. The landscape looked a magnificent sight, bathed as it was in bright afternoon sunshine, but Verity

swiftly discovered that the temperature was not con-
ducive to setting a strenuous pace, and so she merely
strolled towards the home wood, which edged the park
for quite some considerable distance.

The shade of the trees looked most inviting, but she
resisted the temptation to venture beneath those leaf-
laden branches and explore the undergrowth, for a brief
glance back over her shoulder at the mansion, which
looked quite small nestling in its hollow, was sufficient
to inform her that she had already walked some considerable distance, and, having no idea of the hour, she thought
perhaps she ought to be making her way back.

By the time she had reached the lake she was feeling
not just a little fatigued, and decided to sit for a while
to rest her weary legs on the slight bank which surrounded the breadth of glistening water. It was so
peaceful, so completely unspoilt by any of those man-
made eyesores most gentlemen of substance would insist
on having erected on their land. She could quite understand why Sarah Ravenhurst was so blissfully contented
to remain here month in, month out. But then, she suspected, Sarah Ravenhurst would find happiness anywhere
providing her husband was by her side.

Verity's eyes narrowed, but not against the bright
reflection of the sun's rays on the water. Would she be
contented living anywhere? Would she ever come to love
a man with such a depth of devotion as Sarah loved her
husband? Was she, Miss Verity Harcourt, capable of
caring for a man the way Sarah cared for Marcus? Up
until a few weeks ago she would have responded with
an emphatic '*no*'. But now she wasn't so sure.

Something had certainly happened to her since she
had made that eventful journey by mail-coach. She had

changed. She felt, now, strangely discontented with her lot, as though something fundamental was missing from her life, as though she were no longer whole. Was this how Sarah felt when her husband was not with her? Was this gnawing ache deep within really love?

She shook her head, still unsure. The only thing she did know was that when the Coachman was with her she experienced a delicious feeling of euphoria. But how few and far between those occasions! And how long would it take before she could be with him whenever she wished? Certainly not until he had completed his present mission. And she certainly would never expect him to abandon that very important task just to be with her.

Absently, she began to twist the handle of her parasol round and round, sending its adorning tassels whirling in a lively dance. She had never known anyone quite like the Coachman before. She had certainly found him infuriating on occasions, but she had never found his company dull. Which was more than could be said for any other young gentleman of her acquaintance. No, that wasn't strictly true, she amended silently. She was never bored whenever in Brin's company. And he, like the Coachman, possessed that rather unfortunate ability to annoy her unbearably at times. . . How very odd that was!

'Ah, so there you are! And to think I was warning Sarah only this morning that you were likely to get yourself lost.'

Verity turned her head, an expression of exasperation taking possession of her features as she watched Brin, with that elegant long-striding gait of his, coming down the slope towards her.

'Had you been born a woman, Brin Carter, and had lived a couple of centuries ago, you would have been in the gravest danger of being burned at the stake. I don't know how you manage it, but you always seem to appear from nowhere just when I happen to be—'

Verity caught herself up abruptly, but by the gleam of what looked suspiciously like satisfaction brightening his eyes she knew he had guessed what she had been about to admit.

'And I cannot imagine how you think I can possibly be lost when the mansion's looming large not five hundred yards from where I'm sitting,' she finished pettishly.

Uninvited, he stretched himself out on the grass beside her. After crossing one booted leg over the other, he placed his hands beneath his head and looked so comfortably relaxed that she didn't suppose a gentle hint that she didn't require his company would meet with much success at being rid of him, so she merely enquired politely, but with little interest, how he had enjoyed the trip to Oxford.

'Most interesting,' was his rather uninformative response.

This drew a decidedly sceptical arch to her left brow. 'Well, no one would have guessed it. You didn't remain there very long.'

'Evidently you've lost all track of time in your exploration of the grounds.' He opened one eye and peered up at her from beneath the brim of his beaver-hat. 'The afternoon is well-advanced.'

'In that case I'd better return indoors and change for dinner.'

He prevented her rising by placing a gently restraining hand on her arm. 'No, don't rush away. Dinner will be a little later this evening, so you've plenty of time.'

Verity didn't attempt to force the issue. She was

enjoying herself just sitting and drinking in the beauty of the place. 'If common report turns out to be true,' she remarked, breaking the short companionable silence, 'then it won't be too long before you'll be lord and master of an estate like this one. What's the latest report on your uncle's condition?'

'I know no more than you do, Verity,' he surprised her by admitting. 'I've never had any contact with any member of my father's family, not even by letter.' There was a slight bitter twist to his lips, but his voice betrayed complete indifference as he added, 'You see, I'm weaver's spawn, and never mentioned. My father married beneath him and against the wishes of his family.'

'Good Lord, Brin!' Verity was deeply shocked and didn't attempt to conceal the fact. 'To hear you talk anyone would think you were brought up in a hovel. Your grandfather was a wealthy man; he lived in a fine house and was well respected.'

'By those who knew him, yes,' he agreed. 'And he did everything humanly possible to raise me correctly—sent me to Harrow; tried to rear me to be a gentleman; got my commission in the army. But in the eyes of my father's family I continue to remain a pollutant of their noble blood.'

'You sound as though you don't care,' she remarked softly. 'But have you always been so indifferent to their contempt?'

'When I was growing up it bothered me, yes,' he freely admitted. 'There was a time when I did feel bitter, resentful. . . But not any longer.'

It occurred to her then that they had never spoken this way before. When he had joined the army she had been too young, too naïve to discuss such serious topics.

She had almost attained the age of fifteen when he had left Yorkshire for the Peninsula. She had thought herself quite the young lady after spending more than two years at that seminary, but maybe in his eyes she'd still been a child. Was it really any wonder, then, that he had refused to listen to her when she had tried to put him on his guard about Angela? Was it any wonder that her advice had been interpreted as nothing more than childish spite? Or had there been more behind that vicious peal he had rung over her head? Had his resentment at the attitude of his father's family extended to all those born of a certain class?

She gazed once again at the shimmering waters of the lake. If that had been the case, he certainly had set his dislike aside when he had dived into that other lake to rescue her all those years ago.

'You're very quiet, Verity,' he remarked unexpectedly, intruding into her reverie. 'What are you thinking about?'

'My childhood. I was recalling that time you saved my life.'

'Did I?' He looked nonplussed. 'I don't recall that.'

'We were all invited to the Fenners' place,' she reminded him. 'It was their eldest son's birthday, if my memory serves me correctly. A group of us went down to the lake.' Her lips curled into a rather rueful smile. 'You may recall that I was something of a daredevil in those days, so when one of the boys suggested that no female could row across to the other side of the lake and back again, I took up the challenge. I sat myself in the old rowing-boat and they pushed it into the water. No one realised the boat had a hole in the bottom. I'd reached the centre of the lake before the dratted thing began to sink. You heard my cries for help, and dived in to rescue me.' She didn't add that being carried back to the house in his arms had made the whole terrifying experience extremely worthwhile.

She turned her head to look at him. He was still lying at his ease, but that intense look she had seen the evening before was back in his eyes. 'Now that you mention it, I do recall the incident. You owe me a debt of gratitude, Verity Harcourt. . . And one day I may ask you to repay that debt.'

He had spoken lightly enough, and yet she sensed he hadn't been joking. She was about to reassure him that, if it was ever within her power, she wouldn't hesitate to do so, when a plaintive little cry reached her ears and she turned her head in time to see Hilary Fenner crumple to the ground.

They were both on their feet in an instant, but could only watch in dismay as the prostrate figure rolled over and over down the slope, coming to a halt a matter of inches from where they stood.

Hilary's petticoats had ridden up to her knees, revealing an unseemly amount of stocking and lacy pantalets, and Verity could feel a hot flush of colour stain her cheeks, though she noticed that Brin didn't seem in the least disturbed by the sight of a lady's undergarments as he knelt down beside the inert figure.

'I'll go back to the house and get help,' she offered, and was about to set off when she noticed the rather sardonic expression on Brin's face and transferred her attention to Hilary, studying her more closely.

One slender hand was being held in Brin's, the other was resting above her head. The posture seemed unreal somehow, too studiedly elegant to be true. She looked for all the world like a pathetic heroine in some theatrical farce. Then Verity noticed the slight movement beneath the lids. The little wretch was shamming it!

'I don't believe there's any need to alarm the others,' he said, casting Verity a conspiratorial wink. 'I expect it's the heat. She'll soon come round.'

He was evidently offering Hilary an opportunity to redeem herself, but Verity wasn't so charitably inclined. She detested any form of artifice. And this little performance was beyond anything! Hilary deserved to be taught a lesson!'

'I expect you're right. We'll just leave her here, should we?'

'Tut! Tut! We can't do that.' His resigned sigh sounded most convincing. 'I suppose I'll need to carry her.'

'I wouldn't if I were you,' Verity advised, only just managing to keep her voice steady. 'It's a warm day, and Hilary's no lightweight, you know. You might expire yourself before you've gone a hundred yards.'

This was almost too much for Brin. He turned away, his shoulders shaking with suppressed laughter. 'Well, what do you suggest?' he asked with a supreme effort at self-control.

'Give me your hat.'

'What for?'

'I'll go over to the lake and fill it with water, then you can throw it over her. That's sure to bring her round!' Verity was far from surprised to hear the pathetic moan in response to this rather artless suggestion. 'Well, well! I do believe she's coming round.'

'Oh, what happened?' Eyelashes fluttered dramatically before Hilary opened her limpid blue eyes to stare up at Brin. 'Oh, I feel so strange, Major Carter.'

'You'll feel the toe of my boot if you don't stop this

nonsense at once!' Verity threatened, having reached the end of her patience. 'I've yet to witness a more nauseating spectacle!'

Hilary sat upright with remarkable speed and transferred her gaze from openly contemptuous eyes to discover sparkling amusement in brown ones.

'I—I did feel rather peculiar, Major Carter.' She allowed him to help her to her feet, and then flashed a dagger look in Verity's direction. 'No matter what some people may think!'

'In that case, Miss Fenner, I suggest you go back indoors and lie down for a while. I'm sure that is all that is needed to set you to rights.'

His sympathetic tone won him a warm smile. Hilary then risked a rather furtive glance in Verity's direction, saw the expression on her face hadn't altered and gave a haughty toss of her head before stalking off in the direction of the house.

'I don't think she'll try that little trick again,' he remarked, watching her disappear down the path leading to the shrubbery.

'There are times when I'm put to the blush by members of my own sex. What some females will stoop to to attract attention!' The look she cast him as they too set off towards the house was filled with admiration. 'It's a good thing you knew at once that she was shamming it. I was all for summoning help.'

'I've seen plenty of men faint during my years in the army, Verity. And I don't recall any one of them squeezing my fingers slightly.'

'Is that what she did?' Her ever lively sense of the ridiculous gurgled forth. 'What a ninnyhammer!'

'Be that as it may. She isn't going to forgive you in

a hurry for suggesting I wouldn't be able to carry her.'

'I suppose it was a little cruel, as she isn't in the least overweight, but she deserved it after that ridiculous exhibition. I cannot abide shams.'

'No,' he said softly, the look in his eyes bringing a perculiar wobbly feeling to her knees. 'It would never enter your head to resort to such feminine wiles.'

Verity wasn't so sure. If he continued to look at her that way she felt she would be in the gravest danger of swooning herself!

Chapter Eleven

After changing her dress, Verity decided to pay a visit to her aunt's room. When she had returned to the house with Brin a short while earlier it was to be told that Lady Billington had retired to her room for a rest before dinner. Verity hadn't been particularly concerned over this. Lady Billington enjoyed good health, and had never suffered from any of those trifling ailments which seemed to affect so many members of their sex, but she was far from an energetic person, and if Brin had taken the ladies on an extensive tour round Oxford on foot, Lady Billington, never having been a keen walker, would most likely feel genuinely fatigued after the unaccustomed exercise.

Verity entered the bedchamber to discover her aunt, already dressed in one of her elegant evening gowns, seated before the dressing table mirror, having her hair arranged by her devoted Dodd.

'Ah! Verity my dear. I was hoping to have a chance to speak to you before joining the others downstairs.'

'Oh?' Verity seated herself on the edge of the bed. 'Why, have you something important that you wished to discuss with me?'

'No, not at all. I just thought it might be nice to have a little talk in private.' Satisfied with the arrangement of her hair, Lady Billington nodded dismissal to her maid. 'How has your day been?' she enquired after the door had closed behind Dodd. 'I was informed on our return that you had gone out for a walk. I hope you haven't been too bored.'

'Not in the least, Aunt. I've spent a most enjoyable time here at Ravenhurst. And how was your day?'

Lady Billington's lips curled into a strange little smile. 'Very interesting. . . Enlightening, you might say.'

'Oh?'

'Yes, dear. The more I get to know Major Carter, the more I come to like him.'

'Mmm. Yes, he does have a tendency to grow on one, I must say.' Verity took a moment or two to study the nails on her left hand. 'And how did you enjoy the company of the other ladies? Did Lady Caroline majestically lead the way with one of her "We shall go here" pronouncements?'

'Oh, my dear, don't! You'd think. that mother of hers would check her.' Her pained expression was suddenly replaced by one of approval. 'But I can tell you one thing. . . Major Carter isn't the kind of man to put up with any of that nonsense. She tried to ride back with him in his curricle, but he told her in no uncertain terms that she couldn't because he'd already offered to take little Clarissa Gillingham up beside him. He ordered Lady Caroline to get into the barouche and she obeyed, as meek as you please.' Lady Billington chuckled at the memory as she rose from the stool and led the way out of the room. 'Evidently that's the way to handle the earl's daughter.'

So Brin had had enough of Lady Caroline and had opted for a change of companion on the return journey, had he? And what man in his right mind wouldn't prefer Clarissa's company? Verity mused as she accompanied her aunt down the staircase. It also went some way to explain Hilary's ludicrous performance earlier, of course. Evidently she had felt decidedly put out at being the one not to ride with Brin and, being a girl of some spirit, had put her mind to it to have her fair share of the Major's company, though whether or not feigning a swoon was the right tactic to adopt was rather debatable. And, of course, she hadn't fooled Brin for an instant. He might once have been susceptible to feminine wiles, but evidently that was no longer the case.

'Oh, it sounds as if some of the dinner-guests have arrived,' Lady Billington remarked as they reached the hall.

Verity had forgotten that Sarah had mentioned that she had invited a select few of her male neighbours to dine this evening so that Brin would not feel overawed by what would otherwise have been all-female company. Not that Verity thought Sarah need have concerned herself unduly on Brin's behalf; he was more than equal to the task of coping with any company: male, female or mixed. Which was more than could be said for herself! Verity reflected, recalling with a distinct feeling of unease those moments in the garden when his look had turned her knees to jelly. It was perhaps just as well that there were going to be other gentlemen present, if not for Brin's sake...then certainly for her own!

In her confused state it was perhaps inevitable that the first person she noticed on entering the salon was Brin himself, standing by the window, conversing with a jovial

individual whose ruddy complexion betrayed his fondness for port. Their eyes met across the room and Verity
found herself instinctively responding to the smile he
cast her before their hostess came forward, bringing with
her a slender young gentleman of only just average height
whom she introduced as the Honourable Mr Claud
Castleford.

The instant Verity heard the name her ears pricked
up, and she gave the young gentleman, who might not
otherwise have been so favoured, her full attention. Apart
from a pair of intelligent and humorous bright blue eyes
Lord Castleford's son, outwardly, had little to commend
him. He could never be termed even moderately good-
looking and his stature was far from impressive, and yet
within the space of a mere few minutes Verity had
already decided that she liked him. His manner was open
and friendly without being too forward, and she was
more than happy, therefore, to find herself a short while
later seated beside him at the dining-table.

'I had the felicity of making Mr Lawrence Castleford's
acquaintance whilst in London. A cousin of yours, so I
understand,' she remarked after helping herself from a
dish of mushrooms prepared in a particularly fine sauce.

'Oh, yes. Lawrence likes to cut a dash in Society.
Handsome devil, ain't he?'

'Yes, he's certainly handsome,' Verity responded,
betraying in her tone that she hadn't been at all impressed,
and found herself being regarded in no little admiration.

'It's refreshing to meet a young lady, Miss Harcourt,
who hasn't been beguiled by the Adonis in our family.
I'm afraid it's a thorn in my father's flesh that I'm not
more like my dashing cousin. But I much prefer the quiet

life. I'm quite content to remain here looking after the estate.'

She recalled then that her aunt had mentioned that Lord Castleford seemed to prefer his nephew's society to his own son's. There had been no bitterness or resentment in Claud's pleasant voice, and yet Verity felt certain that he must feel a little hurt by his father's most unnatural preference, and she found sympathy coming to the fore.

'That's no bad thing, Mr Castleford. An estate cannot run itself. And what you find to do with your time, I'm sure, is a great deal more worthwhile than cutting a dash in Society.'

'I certainly think so, Miss Harcourt.' He smiled suddenly. 'Not that I haven't tried to play the fashionable gentleman, as you might say. Purchased a racing curricle and a fine pair of greys not so long ago. Deuced foolish thing to have done! Where do I ever go to be seen in such an expensive turn-out? And one needs to be on horseback to get about one's land.'

The fork Verity had been raising to her mouth checked for a moment. It had not been her intention to enquire further into Brin's acquisition of those unmistakable greys, but now the opportunity had arisen. . .

'It is strange you should say that, Mr Castleford,' she remarked in what she hoped sounded an innocently conversational way, 'because I was thinking of acquiring an equipage for myself not so long ago. It was Major Carter, in fact, who talked me out of it. He quite correctly pointed out that I would have little use for such a smart turn-out once I was away from the capital.'

'What a coincidence! It was the Major who purchased my curricle and pair.'

'Really!' Verity was all wide-eyed innocence. 'If only I had known you wanted to part with such fine animals! I believe I would have ignored Major Carter's sound advice had I been granted the opportunity of acquiring such handsome beasts. You are a most remarkable judge of horseflesh, Mr Castleford! But I feel quite out of charity with you,' she went on, for the first time in her life deliberately resorting to a typically feminine trait by casting him a tiny look of resentment from beneath long, curling lashes. 'If only you had made it common knowledge that you wished to part with them!'

'Truth to tell, Miss Harcourt, I did it on the spur of the moment. Ravenhurst happened to mention that his friend was interested in purchasing a curricle and pair, so I asked my father to drive the turn-out to London when he returned to the capital at the beginning of April so that the Major could look them over.'

'How vexing! My aunt and I arrived in town at about that time. I must have missed my chance by a few days only.'

Mr Castleford, without the least prompting, was then obliging enough to tell her the exact date the equipage had been sold to Brin, which turned out to be the Monday after that Friday evening meeting at Frampington. Verity almost sighed with relief. So, as she had always thought, it hadn't been Brin at that tavern after all.

Instinctively she turned her head to stare at the head of the table, where he sat playing host in the absence of the master of the house. Coincidence or not, he happened to be looking in her direction, and one of those smiles which had so affected Ravenhurst's head groom automatically curled her lips.

Lady Gillingham, sitting on the Major's right, noticed

his rather wonderful smile in response, and looked thoughtfully down at the food on her plate. Like Lady Billington, she had been offered ample opportunity to observe the Major during their trip to Oxford, and by the time they had returned to Ravenhurst she was fairly certain that not one of the young ladies who had enjoyed his company during the preceding hours held a place in his heart, not even her own Clarissa. It was a pity because Lady Gillingham liked the Major very well, and would not have been averse to calling him son-in-law, but she did not repine. Clarissa, after all, had only just turned eighteen: plenty of time, yet, for her to meet a suitable *parti*.

Soon after they had arrived back at Ravenhurst she and her daughter had joined Sarah and several of the other ladies in the small parlour. She had happened to be standing at the window, looking out at the glorious view, when she had observed the Major escorting Miss Harcourt back to the house. Evidently he had wasted no time in going in search of her, and it had crossed her mind, then, to wonder whether he had decided, long before this sojourn at Ravenhurst had been arranged, on the lady with whom he wished to spend the rest of his life. Now she was firmly convinced that this was, indeed, the case.

And Verity Harcourt would make the Major an ideal wife. She was a lovely girl who not only possessed a lively sense of humour but was intelligent enough not to bore him within weeks of the ceremony. But was Verity in love with the Major?

She was not the only one to be asking herself this question. Lady Billington too was very much on the look-out for certain signs, for she also had drawn the

same conclusions as Lady Gillingham. She kept half an
eye on her niece while conversing with the Reverend Mr
Martin, who had been placed next to her at dinner, and
later, when the gentlemen rejoined the ladies in the Salon
after the meal was over, she was delighted to see Verity,
without the least hesitation, agree to partner the Major
in a game of whist.

They proved to be a formidable pairing and beat their
opponents, the Countess and the local Squire, very con-
vincingly before offering their places to Sarah and Mr
Martin. Verity, little realising that she had been, and still
was, the cynosure of several pairs of interested eyes,
wandered over to the couch where Clarissa sat in earnest
conversation with Mr Castleford.

'Oh, Verity, Mr Castleford has kindly invited me over
to view his livestock. He has just acquired a Wessex
saddleback. I should dearly love to see her, only—only
I do not think Mama would permit me to ride over on
my own.' Clarissa cast a rather pleading glance up at the
young woman whom she now looked upon as a friend.
'If you were to come too I'm sure Mama would quite
happily consent.'

'Why don't we make up a small party?' a voice suggested over Verity's shoulder before she had chance to
open her mouth. Not that she would have refused the
request, because it would offer the opportunity of putting
Sarah's mare through her paces, which she didn't doubt
for a moment she'd enjoy, but whether she would attain
the same satisfaction from stomping round a home farm
was quite another matter.

'We could pay a visit to the church at Houghton on
the way,' Brin added. 'Mr Martin assures me that the
carvings on the pews are very worthwhile inspecting.'

'An excellent suggestion!' Mr Castleford cast Clarissa a smile of gentle warmth. 'I could ride over to the church and meet up with you there.'

'They seem to be hitting it off very well,' Brin remarked in an undertone as he drew Verity to one side.

She subjected his features to a quick, appraising glance, but could detect nothing there to suggest he might be even remotely jealous. 'I expect they've a deal in common. Mr Castleford, so I understand, enjoys life on his father's estate. And Clarissa too is more at home in the country. What, by the way,' she added as an afterthought, 'is a Wessex saddleback?'

There was a suspicion of a twitch about Brin's mouth. 'I believe, my dear, it's a famous breed of pig.'

'Heaven spare us!' Verity ejaculated, making not the least attempt to hide her mortification. 'Pigs and pews. . . What an enlivening time we're destined for tomorrow!'

Although Verity was far from looking forward to the 'treats' in store, she had no intention of casting a shadow over Clarissa's possible enjoyment and arose in good time the following morning so as not to keep the others waiting.

Both Lady Caroline and Hilary had been invited to join the little expedition, but both had declined: Lady Caroline because she had never been fond of riding, and Hilary because she wished to spend the morning with her mother, although Verity suspected the real reason was because she was still feeling embarrassed over her behaviour the previous afternoon. Consequently, it was just the three of them who went out to the stable yard directly after breakfast to discover Sutton had their mounts ready and awaiting them.

'I got the message to saddle the mistress's mare for you, Miss Harcourt, but don't you be setting 'er to jump no 'edges,' he warned as he assisted Verity to mount. 'She'll take a fence or a five-bar gate, no trouble, but the lady don't take kindly to 'edges. Unseated the mistress not long after she 'ad 'er when Mrs Ravenhurst tried to jump an 'edge.'

'Don't worry, Sutton,' Brin said, drawing Ravenhurst's fine bay beside the dapple-grey mare. 'I'll see to it that Miss Harcourt takes heed of the warning.'

'Miss Harcourt doesn't need you to see to anything,' Verity countered waspishly, which drew a rather nervous chuckle from Clarissa who had overheard the little interchange. 'She isn't so foolish as to ignore sound advice.'

'I do believe Major Carter derives a great deal of enjoyment out of provoking you,' Clarissa remarked as they set off in the direction of Houghton.

'He always has done,' Verity responded, casting her tormentor a look from beneath the rim of the beaver hat, which had been dyed the exact same shade as the borrowed dark blue habit.

'And always manages to succeed so wonderfully well, you'll notice, Miss Gillingham.' Brin's white, even teeth flashed in a wickedly challenging smile. 'Verity, if you haven't already noticed, possesses something of a prickly temperament which makes the occasional goading remark so confoundedly irresistible.'

Verity, at least, noticed the rather apprehensive look Clarissa darted at them, and didn't hesitate to reassure her. 'Rest easy. I have no intention of coming to cuffs with Major Carter. . . Not until we're in private, that is.'

'I look forward to the encounter,' was his challenging response, and Verity decided it might be wisest if she

changed the subject, if not for her own sake then at least
for Miss Gillingham's.

They arrived at Houghton without indulging in any
further slight skirmishes. It was far from a large habita-
tion, boasting only one main street, but there were several
rather neat little shops which looked to be doing some
brisk trading. The church occupied a spot in the centre
of the thriving little community, and directly opposite,
Verity noticed as she dismounted and handed the reins
to Brin, was The Three Swans, the inn she was supposed
to visit if she needed to contact the Coachman.

Her attention was diverted by the arrival of Mr
Castleford, mounted on a sturdy roan. After exchanging
greetings they wasted no time in entering the small
church to inspect the carved bench-ends, many of which
depicted hunting scenes. Verity, surprisingly, found them
most interesting, but it was not long before the thatched
building on the opposite side of the street intruded into
her thoughts. Might Thomas Stone be there now? More
importantly, might this Thomas Stone turn out to be none
other than her elusive Coachman?

The prospect was intriguing, and she found herself
unable to quash the desire to discover if this was true or
not. She had, of course, a very plausible reason for seeking him out: she would be able to inform him that she
now knew for certain that it hadn't been Brin at
Frampington on a certain Friday evening.

After a brief glance at the others, who had moved
further along the aisle, and who were still inspecting the
bench-ends with apparent rapt interest, Verity began to
edge her way back towards the church door. Then, after
a further glance to check that none of them were looking
in her direction, she whisked herself outside, ran down

the church path and across the road into the inn.

It took a moment or two before her eyes became accustomed to the dimness, then she spotted the landlord standing behind the counter and without delay enquired if there was a gentleman by the name of Thomas Stone residing under his roof.

'Mr Stone,' he called to a person seated at a corner table, whom Verity had not noticed before. 'There be a young lady 'ere asking for you.'

Mr Stone placed the journal he had been reading down on the table, and Verity knew even before he rose to his feet and came towards her that he most certainly wasn't the Coachman. Not only was he middle-aged, but he was at least half a foot smaller than the man she had been hoping to see. She hid her intense disappointment quite beautifully, however, behind one of her radiant smiles as she held out her hand.

'How do you do, sir? My name is Harcourt.'

'Aye. Thought it must be,' he replied, gesturing her to a chair. 'We have a mutual friend, Miss Harcourt. And I assume you're here because you have something you wish me to pass on to him.'

Verity nodded as she sat herself down. 'Yes, I have, but I'm afraid it isn't much.' She waited for him to resume his seat and then related what she had learned from Mr Castleford the evening before. 'So, I think you can safely eliminate Major Brinley Carter from further enquiries.'

He didn't respond, and Verity found herself being regarded very thoughtfully, and rather disconcertingly. A rather disturbing suspicion crossed her mind. 'Why are you here, Mr Stone?'

'I'm not at liberty to divulge that, miss,' he told her

rather bluntly, but Verity, far from daunted, gave him back look for look.

'No, I don't suppose you are. But I cannot help wondering who you were sent here to keep an eye on. . . And I would wager a large sum that whoever it was, it most certainly wasn't Major Carter.'

She rose to her feet. 'I think I shall have a serious talk with my uncle when I get back to town. And you may tell our mutual friend that I shall have a thing or two to say to him when next we meet.'

'That message, Miss Harcourt, I most certainly shall pass on,' he said with a ghost of a smile, and Verity, after casting him a further suspicious look, left without another word.

There was something decidedly smoky about this whole business, she decided, waiting for a lumbering cart, leaning precariously to one side under its heavy load, to move away so that she could retrace her steps across the road.

Right from the start she had known in her heart of hearts that Brin was no spy, and, from the time she had informed her uncle of Brin's unexpected departure from town a few weeks ago, she had sensed that Lord Charles had been very well aware of that fact too. And if he had decided Brin was innocent of any traitorous dealings then it was safe to assume that the people working with him must be of a similar mind.

So why had the Coachman encouraged her to come to Ravenhurst and continue discreet enquiries? It just didn't make sense. Furthermore, she could have sworn that Mr Stone was already in possession of the information she had just given him: he too had known that Brin was completely innocent.

So what was Mr Stone's reason for being in the area? she wondered, managing to get back across the road at last. Who was he keeping an eye on? The Castleford household perhaps? But why? Surely Claud Castleford wasn't suspected of being a traitor? No—that was ridiculous! It was much more likely to be Lord Castleford. He worked for the government, and was undoubtedly privy to a great deal of secret information. Added to which, it was Lord Castleford himself who had taken that curricle and pair to London, and it had still been in his possession on that particular Friday evening when that meeting had taken place at Frampington. Surely it made more sense for Mr Stone to be in London, keeping watch on the man who might possibly turn out to be the traitor? How very bewildering!

And that was not all she found perplexing. . . There was something, something lurking amongst the jumble of confused thoughts whirling round in her head, something so blatantly obvious that she ought to see it at once, and yet she remained, frustratingly, blindly groping to capture that elusive. . .something.

Out of the corner of her eye she detected a sudden movement in the churchyard, and just for one blissful moment her spirits soared, but then the tall figure stepped out from beneath the shading branches of the huge cedar tree and she saw that it was Brin.

'And where did you get to, miss?' he asked in that infuriatingly authoritarian tone which he sometimes adopted with her. Added to which, she suspected the question was completely unnecessary, because from where he had been standing he had had a clear view of the other side of the road and must have seen her emerge from the inn.

'Mind your own business, Brin Carter! You're not my keeper. I come and go as I please.'

'Yes, more's the pity!' he responded in a half-growl, as he came to stand beside her and stared down into defiant eyes with a decidedly disapproving glint in his own. 'It's high time you had your wings clipped, young woman.'

At this severe judgement her feeling of irritation disappeared, and a reluctant smile curled up the corners of her mouth as she recalled that someone very dear to her heart had voiced much the same sentiment not so very long ago. How strange that was! Perhaps, though, all tall, broad-shouldered Yorkshire men were innately dictatorial?

'Now, Brin, remove that disapproving look,' she coaxed. 'You don't want to upset Clarissa again. Such a sensitive little creature! Where is she, by the way?'

'Wandering about the churchyard with Claud, gazing at gravestones.' His good humour, too, having been restored, he smiled down at her with a rather rueful twist to his mouth. 'It quite amazes me what interests some people. And here they are! Pigs next, I believe.'

By the serenely happy look on Clarissa's face, as she walked beside Mr Castleford down the path towards them, Verity guessed that there was more between them than several interests in common. Unless she was very much mistaken little Miss Gillingham felt completely at ease in Mr Castleford's company. In fact, Verity would go so far as to say that she had never seen her look so radiantly happy before, and by the time they had made an extensive tour of the Castleford home farm, and were returning to collect their horses, Verity was firmly convinced that Clarissa Gillingham was in a fair way to losing her heart.

'It's a great pity you're expected back at Ravenhurst for luncheon. I would have liked to show you round the house,' Mr Castleford remarked as they entered the stable yard. 'Some other time, perhaps. Unfortunately it cannot be tomorrow because I'm off to the local market town to take a look at a pair of plough-horses and shan't be back until quite late in the day. Pity, really. It's a fascinating old place—secret passages, the resident ghost. . .the lot! I'm sure you ladies would have found it most interesting.'

'I'm sure we would,' Verity agreed, glancing over her shoulder at the grey stone Tudor building. 'Unfortunately we're all returning to London on Saturday, so I'm afraid we'll need to forgo the pleasure. But I hope we'll at least have the felicity of your company again on Friday evening at Sarah's party.'

'Wouldn't miss it for the world, Miss Harcourt! Miss Gillingham has promised to save me a dance, and I hope you also will favour me?'

'Of course, Mr Castleford,' she responded as she once again mounted Sarah's lovely mare which she fervently wished belonged to her. 'I'll look forward to it.'

'I hope you weren't too bored,' Clarissa remarked with an anxious glance at her companions as they trotted out of the stable yard.

'Not at all,' Verity hurriedly assured her stoically, if not entirely truthfully. 'I cannot, if I'm honest, say that I can work up much enthusiasm for pigs, nor do I consider them beautiful creatures, as you and Mr Castleford evidently do, but I must say that this estate is in remarkably good order. Which does that young man great credit. I understand his father leaves the running of his lands to his son, is that not so, Brin?'

He merely nodded in response and she regarded him rather thoughtfully. He had seemed in such a strange mood while they had been looking round the home farm. Surely he wasn't piqued over Clarissa's evident liking for Claud's society? No, she felt sure that this wasn't the case. He had certainly been unusually quiet, though, almost in a world of his own, and yet at the same time watchful. She had caught him on several occasions staring over his shoulder at the Castlefords' house, as though expecting to see someone or something. He really was in a very odd mood. She had never seen him this way before.

'How well do you know the family?' she asked in an attempt to restore his usual good humour. 'Have you met Lady Castleford?'

He turned to look at her this time. 'Yes, a charming lady. Pity she's away from home at the moment. Visiting a sick relative, I understand. I'm sure you and Miss Gillingham would have liked her.'

'I believe Mr Castleford's father is returning before the weekend,' Clarissa informed them. 'He might even arrive in time for the party on Friday.'

'Might he? Now, there's a gentleman I would very much like to meet,' Verity remarked, staring fixedly ahead, and did not notice an alert and oddly calculating look flash into Brin's eyes.

Chapter Twelve

They arrived back at Ravenhurst in good time to enjoy the light luncheon. During their absence Sarah had persuaded her other guests to take a trip that afternoon to one of the local beauty spots and, if there was time, to visit a small town not too far away where she assured them they would discover the most divine little milliner's shop at which she had managed to purchase several very delightful bonnets that equalled anything one could find in Bond Street. The invitation, naturally, extended to those who had visited the Castleford estate earlier.

Brin politely declined, as he had several urgent letters he needed to write, but Clarissa was eager for a further outing, and Verity decided she would go too, especially as Sarah intended making up one of the party.

The afternoon continued dry and bright, but thankfully not too hot, and the gentle stroll through the picturesque wood, which Sarah frequently visited during the spring and summer months, was very pleasant. They did find the time to visit the milliner's shop in the small town nearby, and several of the ladies were eager to part with their money. Sarah had not exaggerated the little establishment's excellence, but with so many eager customers bustling round to view the wares on offer the atmosphere very soon became oppressive, and Verity decided to await the others in the fresh air.

She had only just stepped outside into the bright afternoon sunshine when she noticed a hired carriage come to a halt on the opposite side of the road. Ordinarily she would have paid little attention, but with little to occupy her she continued to view proceedings. The carriage door opened and a man of well below average height, dressed in a suit of black cloth, stepped down on to the road. He was carrying a small wooden box and a rather battered cloak-bag. Verity blinked several times, hardly daring to believe the evidence of her own eyes. Dear God! Yes, yes, it was. . .! It was that French spy!

The hired carriage moved away and she had a clear view of the foreigner as he entered the inn situated a little further along that side of the street. No, she wasn't mistaken. It was he. Her fingers trembled as she raised them to a suddenly throbbing temple. What should she do. . .? What could she do?

'Verity, my dear, what on earth's the matter?' her aunt's concerned voice succeeded in breaking into her frantic thoughts. 'You look as though you've seen a ghost.'

'No, not a ghost,' she murmured, 'but something equally terrifying.'

'What on earth are you muttering about? Don't you feel well?'

'I'm fine, Aunt.' She pulled herself together with an effort. 'Here comes Sarah with the others. I expect it's time we were heading back to Ravenhurst.'

She didn't add 'thank goodness', but she certainly

thought it as she hurriedly climbed back into Sarah's open carriage, while still frantically trying to think of what she could do. There was nothing, of course, except get in touch with Mr Stone without delay. But that in itself would be no easy matter. How could she suddenly announce that she was going for a ride at this time of day without arousing suspicion? Furthermore, she doubted she would be permitted to go off on her own.

For the first time in her life Verity silently blessed Hilary Fenner for being an unremitting gabble-monger. Her incessant prattle offered little chance for the other occupants of the barouche to edge in a word, so Verity's mood of abstraction went completely unnoticed by her eagle-eyed aunt, and by the time they had arrived back at Ravenhurst Verity had been given ample opportunity to decide upon her best course of action: she would get Meg to walk to Houghton with a letter for Mr Stone.

When the ladies began to alight from the two carriages and make their way into the house, Verity dawdled in the rear, and by the time she had entered the hall all the others were heading up the staircase to their respective bedchambers to change for dinner.

She had noticed yesterday during her tour of the house that pens and an ample supply of paper were to be found in the library, but before she had taken more than a step or two towards the comfortable book-lined room its door opened and Brin came strolling out into the hall.

Struck by a sudden thought, Verity stopped dead in her tracks. Brin! She could confide in Brin! If he were suddenly to take it into his head to ride out directly after dinner no one would think it so very strange. After all, men did tend to behave quite inexplicably at times, she decided, taking a step towards him, but then checked again.

She didn't doubt for a moment that he was trustworthy, and she didn't doubt, either, that he would do as she asked, but she knew him well enough to be sure that he would demand an explanation first. And how could she possibly explain things to him without betraying that he had, if only for a short time, been suspected of being a traitor to his country. She recoiled at the mere thought of hurting such a heroic man's feelings. No, she simply couldn't do it!

'Verity, what on earth's the matter, child?' Not only his voice, but his expression too betrayed concern, and she found her fingers suddenly clasped in a pair of strong, shapely hands. 'What has occurred to disturb your peace of mind?'

'Why, nothing!' She was suddenly conscious of the warmth of his touch, and was astonished to discover she liked it. 'I—er—I need to write a letter, but if you're busy in the library I can come back later.'

'And who might you be needing to contact so urgently?' His voice was gently teasing now, but his eyes remained probing, alert. 'I'm beginning to suspect you of clandestine meetings. Have you a secret lover skulking nearby?'

'Wh-what?' Verity couldn't prevent those guilty crimson tell-tale stains from mounting her cheeks, but she at least managed to regain a little composure. 'Don't be ridiculous, Brin!' She extricated her hands from his. 'Who could I possibly know around these parts?'

'That's precisely what I'm endeavouring to find out.' Folding his arms across his chest, he regarded her much as he might have done some wilful child. 'On the evening

I arrived I discovered a letter for you pushed under the door. And lo and behold, when I returned to the house a short while ago, there was another one! Stebbings!' he called across the hall. 'Where did you put that letter for Miss Harcourt?'

The butler came forward bearing a silver tray. The instant Verity saw the bold writing on the letter her resentment at Brin's high-handed tone was swept away by a wave of exhilaration. Ignoring the butler's rather pointed sniff of disapproval, and the quizzical rise of a pair of rather well-shaped russet-coloured brows, she picked up the letter and, after lifting her chin slightly, which betrayed quite beautifully her complete indifference to their censorious views, swung round on her heels.

Conscious that her every movement was being scrutinised, Verity forced herself to walk slowly up the staircase, but the instant she was out of sight of those all-too-perceptive tawny-coloured eyes, she almost ran along the passageway and into her bedchamber. She acknowledged Meg's presence with a vague smile before going over to the window and breaking the letter's seal to read, disappointingly, just one rather abrupt command: *Meet me in the rose garden at midnight*.

Easier said than done, she thought, staring out of the window with a troubled frown. From where she stood she could see the entrance to the rose garden which lay just beyond the formal gardens at the back of the house. She felt fairly certain that the rose garden itself wasn't visible from any of the windows. . . But could she manage to leave the house without being observed?

Of course there was no question of her not making the attempt. And she *must* succeed! she thought determinedly. The Coachman's coming to Ravenhurst had spared her the necessity of trying to contact Mr Stone, but even if that were not the case she would still have moved heaven and hearth to be in the rose garden at the appointed time. . . How she longed to see him again!

'I'm sorry, Meg. I wasn't attending. What did you say?' she enquired, suddenly realising her maid had spoken.

'I wanted to know which dress you wished to wear this evening, miss?'

'Oh, I don't mind. We're dining quite informally. You choose.'

Meg's gentle reminder that it was time to dress for dinner forced Verity back to the present, but her mind refused to remain there for long. She found that throughout dinner it was an effort to concentrate on the general conversation and discovered on more than one occasion, when she had managed to come out of her dreamlike state, that she was being observed rather thoughtfully not only by her aunt, but by the far-from-obtuse Major.

Brin didn't join the ladies in the salon after dinner, but returned to the library to write further letters. At first Verity felt untold relief when she learned that they would be deprived of his company—at least she would have only her eagle-eyed aunt to contend with—but as the evening dragged on she experienced a complete change of heart, and could not help but feel that his presence would at least have provided the leaven to so much dough, as the conversation continued with monotonous regularity to return to the rather boring topics of fashions and household management.

Fortunately the ladies had swiftly accustomed themselves to country hours, and by the time the mantel-clock had chimed eleven most were ready for their beds. Verity,

who had been doing her level best to smother yawns of
boredom for most of the evening, aroused no suspicions
in her aunt's mind when she too said she would retire
for the night. They accompanied each other back up
the stairs, with Verity offering a rather sleepily spoken
'goodnight' as they reached her aunt's bedchamber door,
but the instant she entered her own room she was suddenly brightly alert.

It was not unusual for her not to summon Meg to put
her to bed, and she had made a point earlier of requesting
her maid to lay out her night-gear, thereby making it
quite clear that she wouldn't be requiring her services
again. Lady Billington, on the other hand, always rang
for Dodd, and Verity clearly heard someone enter her
aunt's bedchamber a few minutes later.

Sarah had put all her guests, with the exception of
Brin, whose room was in the west wing, in this part of the
house, and for the next half-hour there was a continuous
parade of footsteps along the passageway outside
Verity's room, accompanied by the opening and closing
of doors, but by the time the hands on her bedchamber
clock showed ten minutes to midnight the house was as
quiet as a tomb.

After throwing a shawl about her shoulders, Verity
picked up a candle and padded across the carpet to the
door. Only a faint click sounded as she turned the handle,
and then she took a tentative glance up and down the
passageway. Thankfully it was deserted. Even the candles
in the wall sconces had already been extinguished by the
servants, which suggested that they too had retired for
the night.

But one could not be too careful, she told herself, as
she tiptoed along the passageway in the direction of the

staircase. If she should be unfortunate enough to come across anyone, guest or servant, then she would merely say that she couldn't sleep and intended selecting a book from the large choice in the library.

Thankfully she was not called upon to give any explanation for her furtive midnight wanderings. The hall itself was deserted, although there was an oil lamp, turned down low, resting on one of the highly polished tables, which clearly indicated that not everyone had retired for the night. Blowing out her candle, Verity placed the holder down by the lamp before tiptoeing across the remaining few feet of hall to the front door and drawing back the substantial black iron bolts which, blessedly kept well-oiled, made only the slightest of grating sounds.

Once outside, caution was forgotten. She sped along the path towards the stable area from where she could gain access to the formal part of the garden. She wasn't at all familiar with this particular area of the grounds, but the moon shining down from a clear starlit sky aided her progress along the criss-crossing gravel paths and she had no difficulty in locating the wicket-gate.

Here, she paused for a moment to regain her breath, and looked about for a sign of the person whom she was longing to see, but she could detect not another living soul. A little further down the path, however, she could see a large shape which looked suspiciously like the outline of a wooden seat, and made her way towards it.

She might at least make herself as comfortable as possible while awaiting the Coachman's arrival. There was no saying how long she would be forced to wait, because he no doubt had needed to travel some distance, but she didn't doubt for a moment that he would come.

Her faith in him was very soon rewarded. No sooner

had she seated herself and pulled her shawl more closely about her shoulders, for the night air was surprisingly quite chilly after the warmth of the day, than she detected the crunch of a footstep on gravel, and turned her head to see that unmistakable outline of cloak and tricorn, and the inevitable red glow from the cheroot clutched between long fingers before it was flicked to the ground.

'Hello, lass,' he murmured in that richly accented voice which she loved to hear. 'I knew tha wouldn't fail me.'

Verity rose to her feet, feeling so insignificantly small as she gazed up at the masked face looming above her but, oh, so infinitely safe now that he was here. 'There was never any thought in my mind of not meeting you,' she assured him softly, and the next moment she was in his arms.

There was nothing gentle in his embrace this time. Fastening her so closely against his tall, hard frame that she was intensely aware of his every powerful muscle, he kissed her hungrily, like some starving man feasting again after days of enforced abstinence. She clung to him, half-frightened, half-exhilarated by the strength of his desire and the ardent need it aroused in her to be held by him, to be touched by him, to be guided by him to wherever their mutual need of each other would ultimately lead.

His erratic breathing informed her clearly enough that he was labouring under immense strain to keep himself under control even before his far-from-steady hands took a hold of her upper arms, holding her firmly at bay when she made to take a step towards him.

'Nay, then, lass. It'll not do,' he warned. 'Don't be tempting me n' more, otherwise I'll not stop next time, and tha'll find thissen on t'ground wi' thy clothes ripped off and missen kissing every inch o' thee.'

It was extremely improper, of course, for him even to suggest such a thing, but she couldn't suppress a thrill of excitement at the prospect all the same. Her rather unmaidenly thoughts were betrayed by glinting flashes of encouragement in her eyes which it took him no time at all to interpret.

'Tha don't know what tha's instigating, looking that way. It's as well that I knows tha's a complete innocent. And that's 'ow tha'll stay until after we're wed.' He felt her stiffen slightly, and saw the provocative sparkle fade from her eyes. 'What's up, lass? Tha's no doubts, 'ave thee?'

'Not when I'm with you, no,' she freely admitted, but was determined he should know the doubts which assailed her when he wasn't there. 'But—but I know next to nothing about you. I don't even know your name.'

'Tha'll learn it soon enough, never tha fear. And don't be afraid I'll ask thee to live in a hovel, lass, after we're wed. Tha'll be mistress of a fine 'ouse. I've plenty o'brass.'

Being thus assured did little to erase those qualms which persisted in tormenting her. 'It doesn't surprise me to learn this. I know you're an intelligent and educated man.' She sighed. 'But I'm also very well aware that you've lied to me.'

He pulled her back into his arms then, and pressed her head against his chest. 'Tha knows I can't tell thee owt, lass. But when this is all over, then—'

'I understand that, and I wouldn't expect you to confide in me,' she interrupted gently. 'But there's no reason for you to tell me a deliberate lie.' He couldn't mistake the almost resentful note in her voice. 'You got me to come to Ravenhurst under false pretences. Both you and my uncle have never suspected Major Carter of being a traitor.'

There was a significant pause before he said, 'Ow else could I'ave persuaded yer t'come'ere. I wanted t'be near thee, lass.'

To be told this was naturally very gratifying, but Verity couldn't help but feel that there was something important he was keeping to himself, something she ought to be aware of herself, but still it continued to elude her.

She thrust frustrations and suspicions aside, however, and wasted no further time in acquainting him with the fact that the French spy had come into the area. Surprisingly he made no response to this intelligence, and she tried to pull away from him, but he kept her head firmly pressed against his chest, as though he feared her eyes had accustomed themselves too well to the darkness and that she would penetrate his disguise.

'I suppose you knew that already,' she remarked, giving up the struggle against the secure pressure of those muscular arms.

'Nay, I didn't know, but I can't say I'm surprised. I don't doubt that 'e's been followed by another o' thy uncle's people, so there be no need for us to concern ussens.'

'It's Castleford you suspect, isn't it? That's why Mr Stone is so close by.'

'Now, then, lass! Tha mustn't be asking questions. But what I can tell thee is no information 'as bin passed on yet, otherwise t' little Frenchman wouldn't be 'ere. He'd be making for one o' t'ports.'

That was a reasonable assumption. It was also reason-

able to assume that she would be seeing nothing more
of the Coachman until this business was over, at least. . .

'I mustn't see you again while I'm here,' she
announced *sotto voce*, suddenly finding it necessary to
cling more tightly to that powerful frame.

'Oh? And why not?'

The question was asked evenly enough, but she
detected a slightly unnerving hard edge in his voice,
certainly resentful and slightly threatening. For all that
he had laughed at her, teased and provoked her during
their short acquaintanceship, she sensed he would be a
dangerous man if crossed. But he was also very percep-
tive, so it would be foolish to try to lie to him.

'Because that dratted Brin Carter is already suspicious
over those letters you've sent here.'

'Is 'e now? And 'ere tha's been saying 'e's nubbut a
dunderhead.'

'Well, he isn't a fool!' Verity announced almost resent-
fully. 'He's extremely astute. . .except where women are
concerned. No, that isn't strictly true, either,' she
amended. 'I believe he's managed to rectify even that
defect.'

There was a short silence, then, 'Oh, aye? Made a fool
o'issen once, did 'e?'

'I wouldn't go as far as to say that,' she responded,
with complete honesty again, 'but he wouldn't listen to
people when they tried to warn him that a particular lady
was not quite as sweetly angelic as he seemed to think.
I tried to warn him. . . And I'll never forget the way he
turned on me.'

'Is that why tha don't like 'im, lass?' he asked gently,
after a further short silence.

'Oh, no. I don't dislike him. In fact there are times

when I like him very well.' The spontaneous admission
came as a surprise even to herself. 'I never for one
moment believed him capable of being a traitor, but there
are times when he does behave in a most perplexing way.'

The Coachman buried his lips in her soft black curls.
'Mayhap 'e's in love, lass.'

'Ha! Not he!' she scoffed. 'Why, little Clarissa
Gillingham has betrayed a fondness for Claud
Castleford's company, but if you ask me Brin doesn't
care a whit!'

'Mayhap she ain't t' one 'e's fallen in love wi'.'

This gave Verity pause for thought. The Coachman
was possibly quite correct, but she couldn't in all honesty
say that Brin had shown any marked fondness for either
Lady Caroline or Hilary Fenner. In her own mind she
felt certain that he preferred Clarissa. Perhaps, though,
his experience with Angela Kingsley had left him slightly
cynical and he no longer looked for love and would be
quite content with mutual respect in marriage.

She opened her mouth, about to echo her thoughts
aloud, but the Coachman arrested her by placing a warning finger against her lips. She listened intently for a few
moments, but could detect nothing.

'You heard something?' she whispered.

'Aye, lass. Best tha goes back inside now. I'll leave
fust. T'sound came from over yonder, where I've left mi
'orse.' He gestured to the area of ground behind the
stable block. 'Iffen there be someone lurking, it's best
'e comes after me. Wait 'ere a few minutes then makes
your way back. I'll be seeing you soon, lass.' And with
that he placed a brief kiss on her lips before darting into
the shrubbery.

For a few moments Verity could detect the rustle of

leaves as he forged his way between the dense branches, then there was only silence. Once again she pulled her shawl more tightly about her, feeling suddenly cold after the cradling warmth of the Coachman's strong arms.

Would it always be like this? she wondered, feeling utterly bereft, totally dejected. Their brief meetings had come to mean so much to her, and yet this time she was left with such a hollow feeling inside, and with the wretched conviction that it was sheer madness to love a man who continued to remain a total enigma.

Trying desperately to dispel her sudden mood of depression, she listened intently, but could detect not a sound, not even that of distant hoof-beats. The Coachman, though, would not foolishly leave his mount close to the house, where it might be discovered. But enough time had elapsed for him to be a safe distance away, she decided, and began to retrace her steps, thankfully without detecting a single suspicious sound and, more importantly, without coming face to face with anyone else. Then disaster struck: the front door refused to open.

Cursing silently under her breath, Verity took a step away from the beautifully carved piece of oak which so effectively barred her entry. Foolishly it had never occurred to her that the bolts on the door might be noticed by a vigilant servant, who wouldn't hesitate to slide them securely back into place. Why, oh, why, hadn't she taken the precaution of leaving a downstairs window open? She chided herself silently for every kind of a fool before a sudden thought struck her. Maybe one of the downstairs windows had been left open? It was a forlorn hope, perhaps, but worth investigating.

She took several more paces back from the mansion and cast her eyes across the long front wall. There were dozens of windows on the ground floor alone, and she had little choice but to try each one in turn. She was about to begin her task when she detected a faint light coming from one of the library windows. Was it possible that Brin was still working in there? Or maybe it was Sarah, for she hadn't retired with the others.

Moving cautiously towards that certain window, Verity saw a chink in the curtains and, placing her face against the cool glass, peered into the room. The gap between the drapes wasn't large, but she could see several candles still burning in their sconces. So, raising her hand, she scratched lightly on the glass with her fingertips and waited, hopefully, but nothing happened. She tried again, tapping louder this time, and almost squealed in fright as the drapes were suddenly thrown wide and a tall figure appeared on the other side.

Unfortunately it was Brin, not Sarah, but one couldn't have everything one's own way, she supposed as she gestured imperiously for him to open the window.

'What in the world are you doing out there?' he demanded, not making the least attempt to speak softly.

'Why, nothing very much at the moment,' was her rather sarcastic response, 'but as soon as you move away I can at least climb back inside. And, for heaven's sake, keep your voice down! Do you want to wake the entire house?'

She thought she could detect a suspicion of a twitching smile about his mouth before he placed his hands beneath her arms and hauled her by rather rough and ready means into the room.

'Have you run mad, girl?' It sounded more statement than question, so she didn't feel obliged to answer, and merely watched as he closed the window and redrew the curtains. 'What the deuce do you mean by wandéring about outside at this time of night?' He looked down at her with all the suspicion of some irate but concerned elder brother. 'It has something to do with that confounded letter, I know. Come on, out with it, my girl, otherwise I might feel obliged to inform Lady Billington of your escapade!'

Alarm bells began to sound. It was no empty threat. 'Oh, Brin, you wouldn't serve me such a backhanded turn, surely?' she almost pleaded. 'No, I cannot believe you'd stoop so low!'

The challenging lift to one russet brow did little to bring any comfort. 'Oh, very well,' she capitulated, if begrudgingly. 'It did have something to do with that letter. I had to meet someone. But you mustn't ask me anything further for the present.'

He seemed to debate within himself for several moments, then said, 'Very well, but you're not to go out alone at this time of night again, understand?'

Verity kept her lips firmly compressed, forcing back the angry retort. He had no right to dictate to her! But then she was hardly in a position to argue, she reminded herself.

'Very well. I won't.' The promise almost choked her, but she forced it out nevertheless.

'As you see. Stebbings very obligingly lit a fire as he knew I'd be working late. I would suggest you sit for a while and get yourself warm.'

Placing his hand beneath her arm, Brin guided her to one of the comfortable winged-chairs placed near the hearth. It never entered Verity's head to protest, even though she knew it was grossly improper to be sitting alone at this time of night with a gentleman who wasn't

a close relative, but she considered their long association
sufficient reason to disregard this edict. Added to which,
she was perfectly certain in her own mind that she had
nothing to fear from Brin.

The realisation struck her forcibly, drawing a deep line
of consternation to furrow her brow as she watched him
move across to the decanters and pour out two glasses
of wine. Yes, she did trust him; she trusted him implicitly.
Perhaps that was why she had never in her heart of hearts
thought that he could be a traitor to his country. Why,
she felt as safe with Brin as she did. . .as she did the
Coachman. . . How very odd that was!

Brin noted the rather puzzled expression. 'What's
causing you to frown so, child?'

'Wh-what?' Verity came out of her perplexing
thoughts with a start. 'Oh, nothing really.' Taking the
glass of wine he held out, she settled herself more
comfortably in the chair, and couldn't prevent a wry little
smile as she watched him take the seat opposite. 'Truth
to tell, I was just thinking that it would appear most odd,
not to say improper, if I were caught sitting alone with
you like this.'

'Not as improper as being caught wandering about the
grounds at this time of night,' he countered, and then
smiled at the guilty flush that accompanied her decidedly
wary look. 'Rest easy, child. I've no intention of carrying
out an inquisition.'

Relaxing visibly, she glanced about the room, her eyes
coming to rest on the pile of papers strewn across the
desk. 'My, my, you have been busy! I hope you don't
intend staying up all night, otherwise you'll be in no fit
state to entertain the ladies in the morning.'

'I'm afraid the ladies will need to amuse themselves.

I shall be riding out fairly early and have no idea what time I'll get back.' He could clearly read the unspoken question in her eyes. 'There are one or two matters requiring my immediate attention. You may not be aware, Verity, but I had an unexpected visitor this afternoon.' She watched his lips curl into a rather strange smile. 'A certain Mr Jessop of Messrs. Jessop, Jessop and Wilkes, my late uncle's solicitors.'

'Late uncle. . .? Oh, I see!' She raised her glass. 'Congratulations, Lord Dartwood.'

'I should prefer it if you continue to call me Brin. I haven't informed anyone else, Verity, and I would be obliged if for the time being you kept the knowledge to yourself.'

She was rather surprised by the request, but didn't hesitate to give her word. 'But you do realise,' she added, 'it will not be long before your new status becomes common knowledge.'

'I know, but just for a while. . .'

She watched him closely as he frowned down at the contents of his glass.

He looked so lost, so like a vulnerable child way out of its depth, that she experienced the strong urge to put her arms round him and comfort him, to assure him that no matter what the world at large chose to think of a mill owner's grandson entering the peerage, she at least didn't doubt that he would be a credit to the name he bore.

'You never wanted the title, did you, Brin?' she remarked with uncanny perception.

'I never coveted it, no,' he admitted, raising his eyes to hers again. 'And, in truth, up until a few months ago I never thought it would be mine. My uncle produced five children, three of whom were boys. The youngest died in infancy. The second son was reputed to be very much like my father—reckless and shiftless. Strangely they both met their fates in the same way—carriage accidents. But that still left the eldest son, Cedric. My uncle must have continued to be fairly confident that the fruits of his own loins would one day take his place. Cedric had married and had produced a child, although a daughter. No one could have foreseen Cedric's unexpected death. He had always enjoyed good health, and it seemed safe to assume, therefore, that he would produce more children. Who would have believed it possible for such a robust individual to succumb to a mere chill on the chest?'

Verity sat quietly turning over in her mind what he had said. She had never heard him ever mention his father before. It was not very surprising really, considering he had died when Brin had been little more than two years old. She had, however, heard enough about Brin's father from servants' gossip and snippets her Uncle Lucius had from time to time let fall to be very certain that she wouldn't have liked him.

Henry Carter had married Arthur Brinley's daughter after a whirlwind romance. Not many weeks after the wedding had taken place, he had left his young bride at his country house and had returned to London and his dissolute life. Brin's mother had died giving birth to him, and his father had not hesitated in placing Brin in his maternal grandfather's care. Whether or not he'd ever taken the trouble to visit his infant son, Verity wasn't certain. All she did know was that Arthur Brinley had thought the world of his grandson, and it was full credit to him that Brin had turned out so well.

'Will you be returning to the capital on Saturday with

the rest of us?' It had been an innocent enough enquiry, voiced mainly to break the silence, so she couldn't quite understand why he should frown at her so heavily. 'I'm sorry. I didn't mean to pry.'

'No, I wasn't thinking that,' he assured her with a gentle smile. 'I was thinking about something else entirely. I don't envisage staying at Ravenhurst for that much longer, but I don't think I'll return to London just yet.'

He fell silent again. Verity knew he must have a great deal on his mind, and, thinking he might prefer to be left alone, she quickly finished her wine and rose to her feet.

'It's time I was bidding you goodnight, Brin. I should hate for us to be caught like this, especially now. You might suspect me of trying to entrap you into marriage!'

It had been intended as a joke, but there wasn't so much as a ghost of a smile around his mouth as he rose to his feet and escorted her into the hall. Without a word he re-lit her candle, and then walked with her to the foot of the stairs.

'Believe me, Miss Verity Harcourt,' he said unexpectedly, his voice a gentle caress, 'I can think of worse fates than being married to you.' He then confounded her further her by raising her hand and brushing his lips lightly across the soft white skin.

Chapter Thirteen

Verity awoke the next morning heavy-eyed and not in the least refreshed. She had passed the worst night she could ever remember. Plagued by dreams of Brin, dressed in cloak and tricorn, one moment taking her ruthlessly into his arms, the next, his features blurred, disappearing in a cloud of swirling grey mist with her hopelessly trying to find him, she had woken several times entangled in the bedcovers, beads of perspiration glistening on her forehead.

The idea of turning over and trying to go back to sleep was tempting, but she thought better of it. At least when awake she had some control over what happened to her, over what she said and did; in her dreams it seemed she had none at all!

Throwing the bedcovers aside, she padded across the carpet to the bell-pull, and within a relatively short space of time was making her way down to the breakfast parlour where she was surprised to discover all the other ladies present.

'Brin's already broken his fast and has gone out somewhere,' Hilary informed her in disgruntled tones after polite 'good mornings' had been exchanged.

'Yes, he said he would be riding out early,' Verity responded without thinking, and received several surprised glances as she took her seat at the table, but it was the ever-vocal Hilary who voiced their curiosity.

'When did he inform you about that?'

Verity discovered she was the focal point of many pairs of interested eyes, but was in no danger of losing her composure as she reached for the coffee-pot. 'I couldn't sleep last night, so came down to the library to select a book. I forgot Brin was in there. He told me then. And before you ask, Hilary,' she went on, a slight edge to her voice now, 'he didn't inform me where he was going, and I wasn't rude enough to enquire.'

It was most unlike Verity to be tetchy in the mornings, and Lady Billington looked at her closely, noting the lacklustre eyes and the rather rigid set to those sweetly formed lips. Something, or someone, had put her niece very much out of humour.

She knew her niece well enough to be certain that it wouldn't take very much to rouse that occasionally ungovernable temper, and decided to intervene before Hilary was foolish enough to say anything further and find herself once again on the receiving end of a rather sharp response.

'Some of us have decided to return to that perfectly wonderful little milliner's we visited yesterday, dear,' she remarked, sliding the plate of buttered rolls in her niece's direction. 'I've made up my mind to have that delightful creation with the purple feathers.'

Little did she realise, but she could not have suggested an outing that could have appealed to her niece less. Not only was Verity in no mood to spend the least amount of time in the claustrophobic atmosphere of that little shop with women who had only frills and furbelows on their minds, but she had no intention of returning to that market town where she might run the risk of coming face to face with that French spy. She experienced no qualms, therefore, in politely but quite forcefully declining.

'Perhaps you would care to come riding with Hilary and myself? We have decided not to go. It looks as though it will be another warm day. It will be much pleasanter exploring the countryside on horseback.'

Clarissa's very kind invitation drew a smile from Verity, but even the prospect of a gallop across the park failed to tempt her. 'It's kind of you, but I think I would prefer to stay indoors this morning. For some reason I didn't have a very good night's sleep. A little time by myself will be sufficient to set me to rights, I'm sure.'

'It always does the trick for me,' Sarah hurriedly put in when Lady Billington looked as though she was about to query further into her niece's unusual lethargy.

Lady Billington's fondness for her niece was evident, and her concern over her well-being very understandable, Sarah decided, but there were times when people just needed to be left alone. Verity didn't strike her as a young woman prone to fits of the megrims, but something had certainly put her in a very subdued frame of mind. It might, of course, be simply just the explanation offered—lack of sleep—but Sarah couldn't help wondering whether Verity's unusually quiet mood might not have something to do with Brin. She had spoken to him briefly before he had gone out earlier, and he too had seemed in a strangely preoccupied state of mind, not annoyed, precisely, but certainly in a world of his own.

She was not a prying person by nature, however, and thought that Verity would be far better if she were left to her own devices for a while, so she gave a gentle reminder to her other guests that they had best not tarry if they wished to return in time for luncheon.

Sarah, too, had planned to go out that morning to visit the sick wife of one of her husband's tenants, and so did not linger over breakfast herself. She was crossing the hall towards the front door a short while later when she chanced to see Verity again, coming out of the library with a book in her hand.

'The others have gone, have they?' she enquired, casting her a warm smile and receiving one in response. 'I cannot say I blame you not wishing to return to that milliner's, Verity. It was quite stifling in there yesterday, and I fear that today is likely to be even warmer.'

Verity's smile turned a trifle rueful. 'I'm afraid I shall always be a slight disappointment to my aunt. I simply cannot summon up much enthusiasm for such trifling things as bonnets and find it immensely tedious shopping for such commodities.'

'Oh, you do remind me of me sometimes!' Sarah exclaimed with a chuckle. 'I couldn't agree more. We'll talk again when I get back, if you like. I shouldn't be too long.'

. . . if you like, Verity echoed silently as she watched her kindly hostess leave the house. Oh dear, had she made it so obvious at the breakfast table that she wanted to be on her own? Sarah was such a lovely person, too!

Experiencing more than just a twinge of guilt, Verity wandered into the sunny back parlour, where Sarah frequently retreated for half an hour's peace and quiet. Seating herself by the window, which looked out on to the formal area of garden, Verity could only wonder at the change which had come over her during the past twelve hours. When she had hurried along those criss-cross gravel paths the night before she had been so excited, so happy at the prospect of snatching a few precious moments with the Coachman again, and yet now she was experiencing such a lowliness of spirits, such a feeling of utter dissatisfaction.

The Coachman's rather abrupt departure went some way in explaining this change in her. But that wasn't the only reason she had succumbed to this rather disconsolate mood, where doubts and uncertainties now whirled round and round in her head making her question the wisdom of her own heart. No, of course it was not! It was the legacy of those rather perplexing dreams.

Why had Brin taken on the guise of the Coachman? Why had she responded so eagerly, with such utter abandon to his kisses? She was very fond of him, yes, even though he too could be quite infuriating at times, just like the Coachman. And last night when he had confided in her, looking so lost now that he had come into the title, she had experienced such a strong desire to protect him from life's knocks.

He had been very much on her mind when she had climbed into bed last night, so it was quite understandable why she had carried those thoughts of him into her dreams. . .

But why such intimate thoughts? That was what was so disturbing.

Brin arrived back at Ravenhurst shortly before noon. On learning that both Sarah and Verity were in the house, he wasted no time in changing his clothes and going down to the sunny back parlour where he had been assured the ladies were to be found.

He succeeded quite beautifully in concealing his disappointment when he discovered only Sarah present, and they chatted for a while about things in general. Then Sarah unexpectedly remarked, 'Are you aware that Verity spent a deal of time with your grandfather when you were in the army?'

'Did she tell you that?'

'Not exactly, no. But she did let fall that it was she who wrote those letters on his behalf when you were convalescing here.'

He betrayed no surprise, and a rather tender smile curled the corners of his mouth. 'Yes, I do realise that now. I knew she was very fond of him—admired him, I think. But it wasn't until I made that recent visit to Yorkshire, and spent an evening with my business partner, Jonas Penn, that I learned that it was Verity, and not Angela, who had spent so much time with the old man.'

A flash of blue outside the window caught their attention, and they both watched as Verity entered the formal garden. Sarah followed her progress along the gravel path, a rather secretive smile curling her lips for a few brief moments before she gave a sudden and almost violent start.

'Oh, great heavens! Marcus has returned!' she exclaimed in anguished tones, praying that her sometimes very abrupt husband didn't say anything cutting to the stranger inspecting his grounds.

She thought she could detect that famous scowl, even from that distance, and groaned inwardly, holding her breath as Verity and Marcus approached each other. She saw him hold out his hand, taking slender white fingers into his own, and was amazed when he suddenly threw back his head and roared with laughter. She might have known she would have nothing to fear: Verity's outspokenness would appeal to his rather dry sense of humour.

'Oh, the little minx has captivated him!' Her mock outrage hid quite beautifully her intense relief. 'Look at the rogue flirting with her! Go out at once, Brin, before he becomes totally bewitched!'

He looked down at her with a mocking gleam in his eyes. 'Oh, yes, and you so worried, I'm sure. But I shall go nevertheless. I want to have a talk with her as it happens.'

Sarah remained by the window, not out of any desire to keep an eye on her husband, but out of sheer curiosity. She watched him take a smiling leave of Verity, and within the space of a few minutes he was entering the room and she was being held in a loving embrace.

'I shouldn't be kissing you at all, you flirt!' she admonished when she was able. 'I saw you outside with Miss Harcourt.'

'What an enchanting little witch she is! I mentioned I was acquainted with her uncle, the Duke of Richleigh, and she said she hoped that I wouldn't hold that against her.' He found himself laughing again. 'I must say I've always considered him a complete nincompoop, but of course I wouldn't have dreamt of saying so.'

'No? Now you do surprise me!' Sarah responded wryly, before looking out of the window again. She caught sight of Brin entering the garden, and her secretive little smile returned. 'Do you know, Marcus, I did Brin an injustice. I believed his wishing to invite certain ladies here was all a hum. But I have come to the conclusion that I was wrong. . . Yes, most definitely wrong.'

'Oh?' His dark brows rose as he too surveyed the scene. 'Well, my love, there's no denying that she's an enchanting little minx. Added to which, I have the utmost respect for your judgement.'

She released her breath in an almost wistful little sigh. 'I'm not as a rule a prying person, Marcus, as you know, but I wouldn't mind overhearing that little conversation taking place out there right now.'

Sarah would have been quite disappointed, for the initial exchanges had been about nothing more titillating than the very attractive lay-out of the formal garden, before Brin with quite remarkable dexterity steered Verity towards the wicket-gate.

She was in the rose garden before she realised it, and was quite disappointed to discover that it was nothing like the romantic setting she had imagined the night before, for not one of the bushes was yet in bloom.

'Why have we come in here?'

'Because we were being observed from the parlour window,' he enlightened her with a twitching smile, while urging her with ruthless efficiency towards that certain bench, 'and I should prefer not to be observed.'

This admission brought a wickedly teasing gleam to her lovely eyes. 'Oh? I hope I'm in no danger of losing my virtue?'

'Not at the moment, no. But many more of those provocative looks of yours and I shan't be answerable for the consequences,' he warned lightly, but she wasn't so very certain that he was joking.

She sat down beside him on the bench, and after a few moments when he didn't offer to speak she asked, not out of any particular interest, more of a means to break the silence, if he had been successful in his errands that morning.

'That remains to be seen,' he answered rather guard-edly, and then went on to divulge that he had decided to sell his grandfather's house in Yorkshire. 'It wasn't an easy decision to make, Verity, but the right one, I'm sure, as I shall no doubt be making my home in Devonshire in the not too distant future.'

Verity experienced a sudden spasm of pain in the region of her chest. She had seen nothing of Brin for several years, but now they had become acquainted again, and had—yes—become far closer than they had before he had joined the army. She dreaded the mere thought that he would not be close by when she eventually returned home.

'I suppose you're right.' Her voice sounded strangely hollow even to her own ears and she wasn't in the least surprised at the questioning glance he cast her. 'No, truly. I'm certain it was the right decision.' She forced a smile, but it was an effort. 'And, of course, you will need to concentrate on your new role in life.'

'Ah, yes. . .the viscountcy. That in itself poses many problems.'

'Oh, Brin! Surely you cannot be worried that you won't match up to people's expectations?' she said brac-ingly. 'You'll have plenty of good people about you, only too willing to offer sound advice. . . Marcus Ravenhurst for one. And I shall always stand your friend.'

The look he cast her was hard to interpret. 'Will you, Verity?'

'You know I will.'

'That's reassuring to hear. Because I'm going to

need a friend to keep me safe from all those matchmaking mamas.'

She couldn't prevent a rather wicked chuckle escaping at this. His past weeks in London had been far from easy, but when news of his uncle's demise became common knowledge his life would be plagued even further by ambitious mothers wishing to bring their daughters to his notice. 'Well, I don't see how I can possibly help you out with that particular problem.'

There was a moment's silence, then, 'Oh, yes, you can. . .simply by becoming my affianced bride.'

For several seconds Verity could only gape at him, feeling certain she couldn't possibly have heard him correctly. 'You cannot possibly be serious!' she squealed, finding a semblance of her voice at last.

'I am, my dear,' he responded with devastating calm. 'Deadly serious. I need time to come to terms with this new role of mine. And you are the only person who can buy me that time. The engagement would not be of long duration, of course. And you could break it off whenever you wished.'

He reached for her hand, and for some inexplicable reason she experienced no desire to draw it out of his clasp. 'I never knew my mother, and, although I far from dislike your sex, there have been very few females I have learned to trust. Sarah, of course, I trust implicitly. And you, my dear girl, I would trust with my life.'

Once again Verity found that her voice was reluctant to make itself heard, and she was forced to clear her throat rather noisily before she could force any words out.

'That, of course, is a rather wonderful compliment. But—but I still think you're resorting to rather drastic measures. A fictitious engagement is not the answer, and

I think a little time for calm reflection will bring you to the same conclusion.'

His sudden shout of laughter took her completely by surprise. 'My darling girl, I haven't thought the solution up on the spur of the moment. I have been planning it for weeks, almost from the moment I set eyes on you again.'

'What?' This was beyond anything. 'Do you mean to tell me that the vast amount of attention you paid me in London was done for the sole purpose of hoodwinking Society into believing that you had a *tendre* for me?'

'Er—not exactly, no,' he responded cautiously. 'But one must try to make provisions for every eventuality. And you must admit that a few lines in the newspapers announcing our betrothal would look most odd if I hadn't paid you any attention at all. Besides which, I enjoyed being with you—still do for that matter,' he added ingenuously. 'It is no hardship being in your company, believe me.'

'Oh, isn't it? You unprincipled wretch!' Verity snatched her hand away, as though to leave it resting in his any longer would run the risk of contamination. 'And what about those poor girls you induced to come here, giving them false hopes?'

'Heaven spare me!' he exclaimed in combined amusement and exasperation. 'You don't imagine surely that either the screech owl or the zombie stands in the least danger of suffering a bruised heart? The only one I might have suffered pangs of conscience over was Clarissa Gillingham, but after watching her making sheep's eyes at Castleford yesterday, that isn't very likely.'

'She didn't make sheep's eyes at him at all,' Verity argued unsteadily, trying desperately hard not to laugh at his rather unflattering descriptions of Hilary and Lady Caroline. 'They merely have a deal in common.'

'Be that as it may. How could I have invited you here on your own? You would only have become suspicious and wouldn't have come.'

Verity regarded him searchingly for a moment. 'Do you know, Brinley Carter, there's a great deal more to you than meets the eye. You're a devious, conniving rogue.'

He betrayed no visible signs of having taken offence at this unflattering description of his character. 'You'll do it, then? We can announce our engagement at the party tomorrow evening.'

'I haven't agreed to anything! And you can stop looking at me like that,' she ordered when he appeared crestfallen, 'because it doesn't fool me for a moment!'

She turned her head away to stare sightlessly at the rose bush directly in front of her. Now that she was over the initial shock his suggestion seemed less outrageously foolish. He hadn't been the only one to suffer from unwelcomed attentions, and she felt fairly certain that when she returned to London, Lady Billington's house would once again be plagued by an endless stream of foolish young men thinking themselves in love.

She found herself, surprisingly, seriously considering his scandalous suggestion. 'We cannot possibly suddenly announce that we have become betrothed,' she said, turning to look at him again. 'If you want to fool people, you must do things properly. First of all, you'll need to contact my Uncle Lucius and ask his permission.'

'I've already done that,' he announced, completely taking the wind out of her sails. 'Took that precaution when I visited Yorkshire a while back. He had no objections. In fact,' he went on, ignoring her astounded look, 'he seemed more than happy at the prospect.'

'I don't believe I'm hearing this.' She shook her head in disbelief. 'Well, you might be able to fool Uncle Lucius, but Aunt Clara's a totally different proposition. She'll see through the sham instantly.'

'I think you'll find you're mistaken.' The wickedly glinting sparkle faded from his eyes and he looked at her intently. 'Will you do it, Verity, for. . .friendship's sake? Will you become betrothed to me?'

Common sense told her it was madness even to consider doing such a thing, and every fibre of her being recoiled against such duplicity, but she found herself saying, 'Very well. But only until the end of the Season.'

'Believe me, my darling, that will be sufficient,' he murmured, his voice as gentle as the lips he placed to the corner of her mouth.

Such a fleeting contact, no more than a brief token of affection a brother might bestow upon his sister, and yet sufficient to bring other and more passionate contacts vividly to mind, sending Verity's pulse rate soaring in alarm.

Dear Lord! What on earth would the Coachman make of all this when she told him. . .? As tell him she must.

Chapter Fourteen

'**A**h! There you are, Verity, my dear.' Lady Billington came out of the small parlour in time to see Stebbings admitting her niece to the house. 'Been out with Major Carter again in his curricle, have you?'

As she had already informed her aunt precisely where she had intended going that afternoon before she had left the house, and with whom, Verity considered the question superfluous and a response completely unnecessary, and merely smiled in a vague sort of way as she accompanied her aunt up the staircase.

'I imagine you'll want to rest before changing for the party tonight. All the other ladies have retired to their rooms. I must say, dear, I'm really looking forward to it.'

You might be, Verity thought, thoroughly disgruntled with life, but I most certainly am not!

She kept her gaze firmly fixed on the hem of her skirt, wondering for perhaps the hundredth time what madness had possessed her to agree to Brin's outrageous scheme. She had been secretly 'betrothed' for twenty-four hours, and hadn't enjoyed a single moment's peace of mind since foolishly acquiescing to the fiasco.

She felt as if she were being torn apart: half of her understood completely his motives and remained steadfastly determined to do all she could to help him as a friend, while the other half recoiled at the mere thought of acting out this farce which was tantamount to cozening people of whom she was genuinely fond.

She had been unable to bring herself to say anything at all to her aunt; but, as Brin had so brutally pointed out during their recent drive round the park, he had every intention of announcing their engagement at the party tonight and considered that she was being grossly unfair not to inform Lady Billington beforehand.

Unfair. . . The word left a rather bitter taste in her mouth. What could be more unfair or more despicable than repaying someone's kindness and loving attention over the years by coming to her with a mouthful of lies?

They had reached Lady Billington's bedchamber door and, as her niece appeared to be in a very pensive frame of mind, she made to enter, but Verity forestalled her by placing a restraining hand on her arm. 'Aunt Clara, would you mind if we talked for a while? I promise I shan't stay long. You'll have plenty of time to rest before changing for the party.'

Nothing could have pleased Lady Billington more. 'Of course I don't mind, my dear. I've seen very little of you during the past two days. It will be pleasant to have a comfortable little coze.' The rather satisfied glint in her eyes went completely unnoticed as she led the way into the room. 'You seem to have spent a deal of time in Major Carter's company.'

'Well, yes. And that is precisely what I want to talk to you about.' The opening had been there and Verity was determined to make use of it before she'd a chance

to change her mind. 'Major Carter and I have—have. . .'
She paused to take a deep, steadying breath while her
eyes remained firmly glued to the pretty pearl brooch
adorning the neckline of her aunt's gown.

'Major Carter has done me the honour of asking for
my hand in marriage and I have accepted.'

There, it was out! She'd done it! The confession,
strangely, brought a deep feeling of relief, but the satisfaction was short-lived. Verity raised her eyes and was
appalled to see tears moistening her aunt's lashes before
rolling silently down satiny pink cheeks.

'No, no, don't cry!' She was at her aunt's side in an
instant and held as much of that plump frame as she
could fit into her slender arms. 'It'll be all right. I promise
it will be all right!'

'Oh, my dear, I know it will. It's what I've been desperately hoping for, praying for these past weeks.'

'Wh-what?' Verity sprang back as though she had been
doused in scalding water.

'He's the very one for you, dear. I've known it from
the moment I first set eyes on him at the Morlands'
party.' Delving into the pocket of her gown, Lady
Billington drew out a wisp of silk and dabbed at her
eyes. 'And these past days, seeing the two of you
together. . . And last night when he hardly left your
side. . . Oh, you've made me so very happy!'

Tears of joy, not sorrow! Verity could hardly believe
it. Fearing her legs would no longer support her, she took
the precaution of slumping down on the spindle-legged
chair conveniently situated a little behind her. She was
well and truly caught in a vicious trap. And, what made
things so much worse, it was a trap of her own making.
When the engagement was broken in a few weeks' time,

dear Aunt Clara would be heartbroken. She simply couldn't win! If her present predicament hadn't promised to lead to rather sad repercussions she would have laughed at the absurdity of it all.

'And, my dear, he's so very much in love with you. Anyone can see that.'

It was as much as Verity could do to stop herself from gaping. Things were getting progressively worse with each passing minute. 'I suppose we have grown quite fond of each other.' It sounded such a foolish thing to say, but she could think of nothing else. And at least it wasn't a lie!

'Fond?' Lady Billington's tinkling laughter seemed to hang tauntingly in the air. 'You have kept me on tenter-hooks for weeks, you wicked girl! And I must say you hid your true feelings very well. But last night I knew. When Brin joined us in the salon after dinner and went straight across to sit beside you on the sofa. . . Well, one would have needed to be blind not to see instantly that you were hopelessly in love with each other.'

This couldn't be happening. It was like some fiendish bad dream. Feeling more than just a little dazed by it all, Verity rose very gingerly from the chair and moved slowly to the door, knowing that if she were forced to endure many more of her aunt's rather astounding utter-ances she would end by confessing the truth. 'I'll leave you to rest now, Aunt Clara.'

'There's no need, child. I'm not in the least need of a lie-down.'

'But I am!' Verity responded with feeling. 'We'll talk again later,' she added, and whisked herself into her own bedchamber with unseemly haste, thereby denying her aunt the opportunity to utter anything further to confound her.

Untying the ribbons of her bonnet with fingers that were far from steady, Verity tossed the confection on the bed and then slumped down beside it, unable to believe the woman whom she had always believed possessed quite remarkable powers of penetration could have mouthed such absurdities. It was bad enough that Lady Billington was overjoyed at the betrothal without compounding such folly by suggesting that anyone could see that they were very much in love. . . Why, it was preposterous! What on earth had they ever said or done to give rise to such a ridiculous assumption?

Leaning back against the mound of pillows, Verity stretched out on the bed and frowned up at the pretty powder-blue silken canopy above her head as her mind went over the events of the previous evening.

They had dined early, as usual, and afterwards Brin and Marcus had enjoyed a game or two of billiards before rejoining the ladies in the salon. It was quite true that Brin had come straight over and sat himself down beside her on the sofa. But what had been so unusual about that? Except for that first evening at Ravenhurst, when she had deliberately avoided his company, and the night he had incarcerated himself away in the library, he had always made a point of seeking her out. Her eyes narrowed as the truth of this hit her rather forcibly. Yes, he had, hadn't he?

Absently gnawing at her bottom lip, she pondered over this rather undeniable fact, and after a minute or two had to own that perhaps there was some justification for her aunt's rather surprising assumption. Until Brin had admitted to it himself, it had never occurred to her that the

cunning wretch had been singling her out for particular
attention. Now, when he announced the betrothal this
evening, no one would be in the least surprised. Oh, yes,
he had been immensely clever; he had paved his way
with such artful dexterity that even she had been blissfully unaware that she had been nothing more than a
skilfully manoeuvred pawn in his rather amoral stratagem
to keep himself safe from the tedious attentions of
matchmaking mamas.

Well, and who could blame him for that? she mused,
smiling in spite of the fact that she had been remarkably
obtuse not to have realised long since. But then, in her
own defence, she would have to own that she hadn't
noticed any obvious changes in his attitude towards her.

Right from that very first curricle ride in Hyde Park
they had, apart from the odd slight skirmish, been on
very friendly terms. Why, anyone with a ha'p'orth of
sense could see they behaved more like brother and sister:
sometimes quarrelling, but for the most part com-
panionably close. Added to which, he had never looked
at her with that doe-eyed, rather sickening look of
devotion most young gentlemen adopted when they had
become captivated by a certain young damsel. And she
sincerely hoped that she had never looked at him like
some besotted, simpering ninnyhammer! So why was her
aunt so convinced they were in love?

Oh, it was all too ridiculous for words! she decided,
swiftly abandoning any further attempt to unearth the
possible reason for the ludicrous supposition and, swinging her feet to the floor, went across to the bell-pull.

Meg took no time at all in arriving in answer to the
summons and Verity, placing herself with complete faith
in the hands of her young and remarkably skilful abigail,

concentrated on getting ready for the party that evening.

After bathing and washing her hair, which took a considerable amount of time to dry as it was quite long, she donned the white dress which she had worn on the occasion of the Gillingham ball. Meg took her time in creating a more elaborate hairstyle for the evening, and had just positioned a spray of artificial white flowers amongst the riot of dusky locks when there was a knock on the door.

Believing it to be her aunt, Verity didn't hesitate to grant admittance. She clearly heard her young maid's sharp intake of breath and, turning her head, very nearly gasped herself.

She had never before seen Brin in the uniform of his regiment, the 95th Rifles. He was an impressive figure no matter what he wore, but in the full dress rifleman-green uniform, with its dolman and pelisse braided in black and with the plain crimson sash about his waist, he looked nothing short of magnificent.

A hard lump suddenly lodged itself in her throat as she nodded dismissal to her maid, and in those moments when she watched Brin close the door behind Meg and move slowly towards her she experienced the most searing pains of bitter regrets.

Having still been smarting over the peal he had rung over her head all those years ago, she had been too stupidly proud, too selfishly spoilt, to attend his farewell party before he had left Yorkshire for Portugal that very first time. He might so easily have lost his life, adding to those many thousands of British casualties—had come perilously close to doing just that at Badajoz.

Yet she had never once taken the trouble to pen him a few lines during those years he had spent fighting for his country, and had always managed to avoid coming face to face with him on those rare occasions when he had returned to Yorkshire on leave. Even after his long period of convalescence here at Ravenhurst, when he had returned home, sadly to see his grandfather for the last time, she had arranged to be away in Kent visiting her aunt, and had thereby neatly avoided having to meet him.

How incredibly petty-minded she had been! What a despicable attitude to adopt towards this brave man who had, after all, told her no more than the truth: she had been a selfish, spoilt creature whose real motive for speaking to him about his childhood sweetheart, if the truth be known, had not been motivated by any desire to spare him pain in the future, but had stemmed from her own petty jealousy.

Brin was not slow to notice tears, barely held in check, moistening her eyes, and took an urgent step towards her. 'What's wrong, Verity?' Placing his hands gently beneath her elbows, he drew her up from the stool and looked down at her searchingly. 'Are you having second thoughts. . .? Regrets?'

'Regrets, certainly,' she admitted, 'but not about the engagement.'

'Are you sure?'

'Well, perhaps one or two,' she admitted softly. 'But I have no intention of rescinding on the arrangement.'

His rather wonderful smile of gratitude caused the muscles in her abdomen to knot quite painfully. 'That's good, because I've informed Marcus and Sarah. They're overjoyed with the news.'

If this was said in the hope of making her feel any easier it fell far short of the mark. 'They're not the only ones. My aunt was quite ecstatic when I informed her earlier.' She had managed to control the threat of tears, but failed quite miserably in trying to prevent the grave misgivings she was experiencing from being clearly mirrored in her eyes. 'I don't enjoy lying to people, Brin. You do realise, I hope, that there are going to be some searching questions asked when we break off our engagement?'

'We'll cross that bridge when we come to it,' he responded in a tone which could best be described as indifferent. 'But in the meantime,' he went on, delving into one of his pockets, 'I hope you will accept this as a token of my...of my very sincere regard for you, Verity Harcourt.' And before she realised what was happening he had slid the sapphire and diamond ring down the third finger of her left hand.

Taken completely by surprise, she could only stare, awed, at the brightly sparkling stones. Never had she seen anything quite so beautiful, or so much to her taste. Just when he had acquired it and just how he had managed to purchase one that fitted so perfectly she could only wonder at. Suddenly the betrothal seemed so real, and for a few moments she was astounded to discover herself wishing with all her heart that it were true, but then common sense prevailed.

'It's beautiful.' The words seemed to graze painfully against the sides of her throat, but she forced them out, none the less. 'I promise I shall take every care of it, Brin, and return it to you when—'

'No,' he interrupted gently. 'As long as I breathe no other woman shall wear that ring. It's yours, and yours alone. No matter the outcome.' And before she could enquire what he meant, he had placed his hands on her sides and his head lowered.

Verity was too stunned by her traitorous body's immediate response to put up even a token resistance. Those shapely hands, by accident or design, were gently pressing against the sides of her breasts, sending wave upon wave of such sensual pleasure to ripple throught her that when his lips merely brushed across hers in a repeat of the salute he had bestowed in the garden the day before, she found herself suffering pangs of disappointment.

'Well, that seems to have put some colour back into your cheeks,' he remarked, betraying more than just a little satisfaction, and Verity discovered she was powerless to prevent the telltale guilty blush from deepening; as powerless as she was to untangle those wildly conflicting emotions which seemed to have entwined round her brain, successfully preventing any coherent thought save one—she desperately wanted him to kiss her again.

Evidently, though, he felt no similar yearning, for he moved away to collect her fringed silk shawl and placed it about her shoulders. 'Sarah suggested that you might like to remain here with me after the others have left tomorrow. It's entirely up to you, of course, and I shan't press you.'

Verity discovered herself incapable of making even this simple decision and turned towards him seeking guidance, just as though it were the most natural thing in the world for her to do so. He seemed to understand without being told that she was unsure of what to do, so made up her mind for her.

'I think it would be best if you remain. You'll only be plagued to death by the curiously vulgar element in Society if you go back with your aunt. I shall arrange for a few lines to appear in the Morning Post, so that by the time we return all the tattle-mongers will have been apprised of our betrothal and might just leave us in peace.' He had no difficulty in detecting doubts and uncertainties, not to mention bewilderment, flit over her face. 'And a few days' peace and quiet is precisely what you're urgently in need of.'

There was no arguing with this, and when Brin, taking her completely by surprise for a second time, announced their engagement as soon as they entered the drawing-room where everyone had congregated before dinner, she felt that weeks, not days, of peace and quiet would be needed to restore her to a semblance of her former self-possessed state.

Only by dint of tapping into that hitherto untouched inner reserve of iron determination did she manage to appear outwardly composed, and she could only marvel at Brin's quite remarkable sang-froid, accepting all the heartfelt congratulations with such an air of spontaneous gratification that Verity had forcibly to remind herself on more than one occasion that their betrothal was pure fabrication.

Had she not been standing right beside him, listening to his every word, watching his every gesture, she would never have believed it possible for someone to sound so utterly convincing. He really was quite superb. A born actor, in fact!

He responded to the various questions one or two of the more inquisitive ladies threw at him without so much as a pause for consideration, but when, during dinner, Lady Westbury enquired when the wedding would be taking place, and he blithely responded that he wasn't in favour of long engagements, and that it would be within weeks rather than months, Verity came perilously close

to choking on a piece of game pie and was determined
to check him at the first available opportunity before he
carried things too far.

'What the deuce do you mean by telling people the
ceremony will take place soon?' she demanded in an
undertone when, directly after dinner, they all made their
way across the hall to the large salon where the party
was to be held. 'You're digging a very big hole for
yourself,' she continued, nettled by his continued self-
assured air. 'And don't expect me to aid you if you find
yourself unable to get out!'

'You'll hardly be in a position to, my darling girl,'
he pointed out, his composure completely unruffled, 'as
you'll be trapped in there with me. Now, stop glowering
at me like an infuriated kitten and go over and talk to
your aunt, there's a good girl. She's trying desperately
to attract your attention. I'll come back to you in plenty
of time for the first waltz.' And with that he added insult
to injury by giving the back of her arm a nip with his
fingertips.

If he could feel her eyes boring into his back like
dagger-points he betrayed no visible sign as he moved
away to speak to the first of the Ravenhursts' neighbours
to arrive, and Verity, looking far from a blissfully happy
bride-to-be, went over to her aunt, who was chatting
away to Mrs Fenner and her daughter.

'Why, you look as if you've had a lovers' tiff!' Hilary
screeched, with such a look of malicious satisfaction that
Verity could have hit her.

'I wouldn't go as far as to say that,' she responded
with careful restraint. 'But I have never been one to turn
a deaf ear when someone is deliberately going out of his,
or her, way to irritate me, as you very well know, Hilary.'

Although not the most tactful of people, Hilary was far from slow-witted and sensibly refrained from saying anything further to annoy her rather quick-tempered neighbour before moving away with her mother to mingle with the other guests.

'Sarah tells me you're remaining here at Ravenhurst, dear,' Lady Billington remarked, quickly guiding Verity towards two unoccupied seats where they could sit quietly for a while in private. 'I've no objection, of course, if that's what you want.'

'Oh, I'm sorry, Aunt Clara. I meant to tell you before we went in to dinner, but it completely slipped my mind. I haven't had the opportunity to discuss it with Sarah as yet, either. It was Brin's idea. He sort of made the decision for me.'

This was music to Lady Billington's ears. She had always had complete faith in the Major's ability to bridle a headstrong filly, and he had evidently already made a start, though she wisely chose not to voice her satisfying reflections aloud, and merely said, 'I didn't realise you intended announcing your betrothal so early in the evening. It took me quite by surprise.'

'You're not the only one,' came the rather disgruntled response, and she looked at her niece closely.

'I didn't realise, either, that you were only contemplating a short engagement?'

'Oh, it will be short, right enough,' Verity confirmed, her teeth set rigid in hard determination. *A lot shorter than he thinks if he carries on as he has been doing!* she added silently.

The quartet of musicians hired for the evening struck up and the object of Verity's far from flattering thoughts came across to claim her for the first dance. The party which had been originally planned merely as an informal social gathering had now changed to one celebrating their 'betrothal', and for a short while they had the floor to themselves, the cynosure of all eyes, but then much to Verity's intense relief other couples began to join them.

She began to relax slightly, but still felt very conspicuous, and remained quite out of charity with the man who, she was very well aware without being told, had already taken it upon himself to organise her life.

'If you don't take that mulish look off your face, my girl, I'll kiss you right here in the middle of this dance-floor.'

It was no idle threat, but Verity refused to be cowed. 'You dare,' she hissed like a spitting kitten, 'and I'll retaliate by boxing your ears soundly. And then folk will begin to realise this engagement is not quite what it appears to be!'

His response was to throw his head back and roar with laughter which, of course, was not quite the effect she'd had in mind. Several indulgent smiles were cast in their direction, and she found to her surprise that she couldn't help smiling herself. It was a complete waste of effort trying to be angry with him for any length of time. He really was a hopeless case! He never behaved as she expected and, what was worse, seemed to possess an innate ability to make her furiously angry one minute and blissfully contented the next.

Her smile widened as she gazed up at his handsome face with its crowning mane of reddish brown hair which swept back in gentle waves from a high, intelligent forehead. She studied each attractive feature in turn and found herself loving the way his eyes crinkled at the corners whenever he smiled, just as they were doing now.

'You are a darling, you know,' he said unexpectedly, and so impersonally that he might have been remarking on nothing more interesting than the weather, but the compliment lost nothing for all that. 'It's a wonder you weren't snapped up years ago.'

'I've more sense, that's why. It's quite an art avoiding parson's mousetrap. But you know that yourself, as you've succeeded in doing so thus far. And, of course,' she went on after he had executed a rather neat turn in order to miss a collision with Hilary and her rather energetic young partner, 'that is in essence the reason we find ourselves indulging in this mindless folly.'

Instinctively her eyes moved towards the door, where the Ravenhursts stood greeting new arrivals. 'Surely you've at least told Marcus and Sarah the truth?'

There was a significant pause before he said, 'Naturally,' and she looked at him sharply, unsure whether to believe him or not.

'And do they also know about your coming into the title?'

'Yes. I've informed them about that too. Like yourself, they are completely trustworthy. You can safely tell either of them anything and be certain it will go no further. I hope that during your stay here you'll become better acquainted with Marcus. He can be an abrupt devil at times, but you're too discerning to be put off by an astringent remark or two. Once you get to know him I'm certain you'll like him. He's one of the finest men—'

Verity noticed his eyes narrow fractionally and turned her head in the direction of his rather penetrating gaze to see Lord Castleford, accompanied by his son and nephew, enter the room. Why should their arrival cause Brin to lose track of what he had been saying and bring a rather thoughtful expression to his face? She looked back at him, only to discover him smiling down at her once again.

'Clarissa will no doubt be pleased now that Claud has arrived.'

'And does that concern you?'

'Good heavens, no! Why on earth should it?'

It shouldn't, Verity thought as the dance came to an end and they began walking back towards Lady Billington. But something had certainly brought that flicker of thoughtful concern into his eyes, and if it wasn't Claud's arrival. . .then whose arrival had engendered that wary look?

It just so happened that her aunt was conversing with Lady Gillingham and her daughter, and Brin exchanged a brief word with each of the three ladies before moving away to ask Lady Caroline to dance. If Clarissa felt a little aggrieved at being passed over in preference to the earl's daughter she certainly betrayed no visible signs of it as she gazed fleetingly at the Castleford family, who remained in earnest conversation with their host and hostess, and then looked rather wistfully down at her hands resting in her lap.

Verity smiled to herself as she sat down beside her. 'He's a very personable gentleman. It's little wonder you like him.'

Clarissa made not the least attempt to dissemble, although a rather fetching blush mounted her cheeks. 'Yes, I like him. He's not handsome or dashing, like his cousin, but I like him so very much better.'

Verity frowned slightly at this. 'You do not care for his cousin either, then?'

'No, not very much,' Clarissa admitted. 'I find him

rather arrogant. And he has such a coldly calculating look that always managed to send shivers down my spine whenever I danced with him in London. I don't know him that well, of course, and perhaps one shouldn't make snap judgements because one can so often be wrong with first impressions.'

'True. But I don't think you're so very far out in your assessment of him.'

'And I wasn't so very far out in my assessment when I told Mama that Major Carter was very fond of you. But then she knew that already. I'm so very happy for you, Verity. I think you and Major Carter are very well suited. You get along together so well.'

This was no more than Verity had decided herself earlier, but to hear someone else say much the same thing and to realise that others had come to the conclusion long since was quite disturbing. It wasn't like her to be so obtuse, and she couldn't help wondering what else others had glimpsed in her relationship with Brin which had not been patently obvious to herself, and perhaps still wasn't.

Alarm bells began to sound, but before she was given time to interpret their cautionary message, she noticed Claud and his cousin heading in their direction. Something made her cast a quick glance in Brin's direction. He was still swirling the earl's daughter round the floor. It was not really surprising to discover they were not conversing—after all, Lady Caroline seemed incapable of stringing more than four words together at any one time—but it was rather strange to discover him not concentrating on his partner at all, but staring quite pointedly in her direction with a look in his eyes that, had she not known better, appeared to be almost a warning.

'I trust you were successful in your endeavours yesterday, Mr Castleford?' she remarked, addressing herself to Claud, as Clarissa seemed incapable of doing anything except smile rather shyly.

Lawrence Castleford took out his snuffbox and flicked open its lid with a practised finger while his lips, Verity noticed, were fixed in a faintly disdainful smirk. 'Hardly an appropriate topic of conversation, Claud,' he remarked, cutting across his cousin's enthusiastic description of the two fine plough-horses he had acquired the day before, 'especially as we have yet to felicitate Miss Harcourt on her betrothal.'

Although Verity disliked becoming involved in things that did not directly concern her, she discovered she could not sit by and watch poor Claud, with quite malicious intent, being put out of countenance and came to his aid.

'On the contrary, Mr Castleford,' she said, transferring her gaze to those soulless blue eyes. 'Miss Gillingham, for one, would be far more interested in listening to your cousin expound on the merits of his latest acquisitions than being forced to endure further conversation about my engagement, of which too much has been spoken already. So,' she added, rising to her feet, 'emboldened as I am by the fact that I shall very shortly be irrevocably joined in wedlock, I do not demur at asking you to partner me in a dance.'

Unfortunately her brazen attitude, far from shocking him, seemed to afford him a deal of sardonic amusement. Worse still was his slow, over-familiar appraisal of her figure as they walked on to the dance floor, which left Verity in little doubt that he knew precisely what she looked like without her shift.

Heavens above! she mused as he placed his hand

with studied expertise on her narrow waist. Was that the warning Brin had been trying to convey? Had she inadvertently encouraged the advances of a hardened rake?

'I didn't realise, sir, that you were planning a visit to your uncle's home this weekend,' she remarked, managing to draw his eyes away from their insolent contemplation of her evening gown's low neckline. 'I wouldn't have thought that pastoral serenity was much to your taste.'

'On the contrary, Miss Harcourt, I have a great fondness for Castleford Grange. Both my parents died when I was very young and I was reared in that house. I have been brought up to consider it my home and continue to make frequent visits.' Verity watched his eyes momentarily stray in his cousin's direction and narrow fractionally. 'Claud appears to be rather taken with the Gillingham chit.' His unpleasant smile, rather twisted and contemptuous, returned. 'Well, well! Life is full of surprises! I didn't realise my little cousin had it in him to attract a charmer.'

Poor Claud! How much back-stabbing had he been forced to endure from his elder and more sophisticated cousin during those years when they had been growing up together? A great deal, she suspected. Even now he probably had to contend with a continual barrage of barbed remarks whenever his cousin came to stay. Lawrence Castleford was undeniably a strikingly handsome man, but had little else to commend him as far as she was concerned.

She took a moment or two to study those exquisitely chiselled features more closely and could quite understand what Clarissa had meant, earlier, as she too experienced a frisson of fear scud its way down the length of her spine as she continued to watch him intently. He was staring in Claud's direction again and there was something rather more than cool contempt in that look of his: something quite calculatingly sinister.

She somehow managed not to betray her avid distaste of his company, but was far from sorry when the dance came to an end and he restored her to the protection of her aunt's side. No sooner had he moved away than a deep voice murmured in her ear, 'Be careful of that one, my little love. It's perfectly in order for you to dance with him, but never, I repeat never, be foolish enough to find yourself alone with him.'

Had Brin proffered that piece of sound advice a few days earlier she might well have told him to mind his own business, or at the very least teased him over possible feelings of jealousy, but as she turned and looked up into his face, easily detecting disquiet there, she felt the desire to do neither.

'Fortunately he isn't a frequent visitor to this house,' he went on, following Lawrence's sauntering progress across the room. 'My friend Marcus, being a man of considerable discernment, doesn't encourage his visits. But one never knows. Castleford just might take it into his head to pay a call whilst you are here.'

'Don't worry, Brin,' she didn't hesitate to reassure him. 'I've already come to the conclusion that he's definitely not to be trusted.' She too peered in Lawrence's direction and watched him leading a young lady on to the floor, and was certain in her own mind that beneath that highly polished and prepossessing exterior beat the heart of a poisonously corrupt man.

'Do you know, I think he would be capable of almost

anything. The look he cast poor Claud was—well—filled with enmity.'

'There's certainly no love lost between them. But don't be concerned for Claud. That young man might surprise you. Believe me, he's quite capable of looking after himself.'

No more was said on the matter, and for Verity's part she was quite content to forget that Lawrence Castleford was even present. This was not difficult to achieve, for, when not dancing with one of the Ravenhursts' neighbours, Brin rarely left her side, and she was quite surprised to discover, as the evening drew to a close, that she had thoroughly enjoyed the occasion which she had been so dreading earlier in the day.

Guests began to depart, and Lady Billington too rose to her feet. 'It is time I was thinking of retiring, dear. I have no intention of making a very early start in the morning, but I do not wish to leave it too late. When will you be returning to the capital?'

'Do you know, I've absolutely no idea. I've hardly exchanged above a dozen words with Sarah all evening. Which is quite understandable, really—she has been so occupied with her other guests. And I cannot recall that Brin gave me a specific date. I'll ask him.' She turned and was surprised not to find him hovering nearby. 'Oh, he's disappeared somewhere.'

'I thought I saw him wander outside to the terrace a few minutes ago.' Lady Billington smiled to herself, more than just a little satisfied with the Major's attentiveness towards her niece throughout the evening. 'Why not go and ask him? You can let me know in the morning.'

Verity needed no second prompting. He stood at the far side of the terrace, one booted foot on the low stone balustrade, one elbow resting on his bent knee, a cheroot between his fingers, and was staring out at what little could be seen of the parkland. How many times had he adopted just such a negligent pose when out in the Peninsula? Yet she suspected that his relaxed stance was highly deceptive, that his senses, finely tuned after years of warfare, remained ever-alert.

And she wasn't wrong. He turned his head suddenly, as though sensing he was not alone, and that warm smile that she had glimpsed so often when he looked in her direction reached his eyes, crinkling the corners and intensifying the warmth in those brown depths.

As she came to stand beside him she watched him flick the half-finished cheroot over the balustrade. 'There was no need to do that.'

'I know you ladies aren't enamoured of the habit, but it's one I seem unable to break. Sarah dislikes it intensely, but she's kind enough to allow me to indulge myself.'

The curl came so naturally to Verity's lips that she was hardly aware she was returning his smile. 'Personally I don't object, but even if that were not the case, I still wouldn't have the right to dictate how you should go on.'

'Now that's most odd,' he responded with a provocative lift of one brow, 'because I feel I have every right to govern your behaviour.'

Verity was only too aware that he wasn't joking, and yet she couldn't find it within herself to be angry, or even moderately annoyed, but she managed to say with an attempt at conviction, 'I wouldn't advise you to try. You must remember that we are not really betrothed, although. . .' she shook her head in wonder. . .'there were times this evening when I was forced to remind myself that our engagement was pure fabrication. It appeared so real, somehow.'

'But it is real, Verity.'

His assertion seemed to hang in the air like a softly taunting reminder of how incredibly naïve she had been not to have realised before that there had been no pretence, no playacting on his part throughout the evening. He had behaved quite naturally, simply because to him their betrothal was in deadly earnest. . . And to her. . .?

'And you want it to be real too, don't you?' He gave her no time to answer, but then he really didn't need to; had he retained any misgivings, her eager response to his lips as they fastened on hers with a possessive hunger would have dispelled them at once.

Verity wasn't certain whether the soft little moan of pleasure came from him or herself as his tongue began to explore the soft lining of her mouth and his hands burned a trail of sensual pleasure down the length of her back to the swell of her hips, holding, moulding her slender body so close to his that she didn't know where she ended and he began. The feel of him, the taste of him, the powerful masculinity of him engulfed her, a heady brew sending her senses reeling with an all-consuming desire for more. . .oh, much, much more.

As a young girl on the verge of womanhood she would have given almost anything to be locked in this man's arms. Now that sweetly remembered yearning, thrust aside by the passage of time, but never completely eradicated, was being fulfilled. And it felt so right, so wonderfully perfect that she knew with a clear-sighted conviction that they belonged together, bound by the unbreakable ties of an enduring love that would stand the test of time.

His body shook in gentle, silent laughter as he dragged his mouth reluctantly from hers to burn a trail of feather-light kisses to her temple. 'You took me roundly to task earlier, my love, for remarking that the wedding would take place soon, but I think you'll now be forced to agree that for both our sakes it would be a grave mistake to wait. I am a man, with a man's very natural instincts and desires.' His smile was rueful. 'My gentlemanly inclinations only stretch so far, and you have strained them to their farthest limits during these past weeks.'

Tilting up her chin, he looked down into eyes that glowed with all the love she bore him. 'I've been determined to have you almost from the moment I saw you again. I could hardly believe it was you, but the hair, the eyes hadn't changed, only it was a woman I looked upon, not a girl. And you're my woman, Verity. You always were mine. And no other man shall have you. That I swear!'

His words, spoken with such fervour, ought to have filled her with untold joy, but the message was achingly familiar, striking a chord of memory that sent ice-cold darts of self-disgust to pierce every fibre of her being.

She wrenched herself away, unable to believe what had just taken place between them, unable to believe what she had so heartlessly allowed to happen. 'I can't. . .I never meant. . .' Each word burned her throat, corrosive as acid. 'Oh, God, what have I done? There's someone else. Brin, forgive me. . .but there's someone else.'

He took a step towards her, searching her distraught features, but she backed away, her tear-filled eyes wild with a seemingly intensifying horror. 'No, my darling, there's no one else,' he assured her softly. 'It is—'

He got no further. She swung away and fled back inside the house before he could reach her. He checked in his pursuit at the long French window and watched her headlong flight across the salon, knowing with heart-rending certainty that her tears couldn't be held in check for long, and that he alone was responsible for the needless suffering.

'It isn't you who should be begging forgiveness,' he murmured, turning back to stare into the darkness. 'But will you ever forgive me...now?'

Chapter Fifteen

Verity forced open her slightly swollen, red-rimmed eyes and was surprised to find her maid standing beside the bed, looking down at her in some concern. It was most unlike Meg to attend her mistress first thing without being summoned, but a swift glance at the clock was sufficient to explain the unusual behaviour.

'Good heavens! Is that the time!' Not even when in London had Verity risen so late, but then she had never taken so long to fall asleep before. She had heard the servants moving about, busily attending to their early-morning duties, before she had finally managed to stem what had threatened to be an inexhaustible flow of tears and had surrendered herself to the healing powers of slumber. Not that sleep had had any obvious soothing effect upon her weary body and tortured mind, but at least she had come to accept, cruelly painful though it was, the only course of action open to her.

Suddenly aware that Meg had not moved, and was still regarding her rather pensively, Verity forced herself back to the present. 'Has Lady Billington left yet?'

'Yes, miss. An hour or so ago. She wanted to see you

before she went, but Major Carter said he would pass on her farewells.'

Just the mere mention of his name brought yet another wickedly piercing stab of pain to that already irreparably bruised and battered area just below her ribcage. So what agony was she likely to suffer when she came face to face with him again? She placed a hand to her throbbing temple. It didn't bear thinking about, and yet she knew she couldn't put off that inevitable interview indefinitely.

'Is the Major in the house, Meg?'

'No, miss. He went off somewhere with Mr Ravenhurst not long after your aunt's departure.'

So, she had been given a respite, had she? She wasn't so very sure whether this was such a very good thing, because she had to face him some time and the sooner that painful interview was over the better. And how much had he guessed already? He was certainly no fool, and although she felt fairly sure that she had not mentioned the Coachman directly, she had managed to tell him that there was someone else, someone who meant as much to her as Brin himself did. . . Oh God! What was she to do. . .? What could she do?

Meg's request as to whether to lay out the sprigged muslin brought Verity back to the present, once again but her mind continued to weigh so heavily with the heartbreaking course of action she was being forced to take that anyone with a ha'p'orth of sensibility could tell instantly that there was something drastically wrong.

Sarah, seeing her for the first time just before luncheon, was not slow to perceive the telltale signs of strain. She had witnessed Verity's headlong flight up the stairs the previous evening, and had glimpsed the unmistakable look of deep concern on Brin's face when he had come in from the terrace, and had assumed they had been indulging in a lovers' tiff. Now she was far from certain that that was all it had been. She seriously suspected that it was something far more serious, but she had no intention of prying. Added to which she had the utmost confidence in Brin's ability to sort everything out.

'Marcus has dragged your fiancé away to watch a mill taking place in a field just the other side of Oxford,' she said, entwining her arm through Verity's as they went across the hall to the dining-room. 'Though how anyone can gain pleasure in watching grown men indulging in a bout of fisticuffs, I'll never know!'

The scathing condemnation did manage to draw a smile from Verity. 'It does seem strange, certainly. But I for one wouldn't attempt to deny gentlemen their amusements, very odd though some of them are, and I suspect you wouldn't either.'

'Very true. But the wretches have left us to our own devices for the whole day. They are not due back until late this afternoon. I must pay a call on the Reverend Mr Martin later, Verity. Would you care to accompany me?'

'If you wouldn't mind, Sarah, I think I would prefer to exercise that darling mare of yours again. I'm not usually a slug-a-bed, but I'm now being punished for my laziness with a slight headache. A good gallop across the park will set me to rights.'

Sarah wasn't so certain, but made not the least attempt to dissuade her, and half an hour later she stood watching her young guest cantering across the park in the direction of the home wood before getting into the carriage and setting off on her own visit.

Without conscious thought Verity turned Sarah's mare on to one of the many paths that criss-crossed the wood and found some relief from the heat of the afternoon sun beneath the shading canopy of the dense foliage, but she knew that the sun's bright rays had little to do with the throbbing ache which persisted at her temples. Until she had spoken with Brin, had tried to explain what had been happening to her during the past weeks, she knew there would be no relief whatsoever. She hoped, prayed he would understand, but even that might be too much to expect. After all, she hardly understood herself just how she had managed to get into such a tangled emotional mess.

She would have been the first to admit that in many ways she had been more fortunate than most. Spoilt, both Brin and the Coachman had called her, and they were right, of course. Even though she had lost both her parents at a young age she had still had people about her—Uncle Lucius and dear Aunt Clara, to name but two—who had continued to do everything humanly possible to make those years while she had been growing into womanhood as happy and carefree as they could.

Even her dear mother, bless her, had ensured that her sole offspring need never marry unless she chose to do so. Under the terms of the will Verity came into a substantial inheritance upon marriage or reaching the age of one-and-twenty. Safe in this knowledge, Verity had never seriously looked for a suitable mate. She had known many young men whom she had liked very well, but not one with whom she could have contemplated spending the rest of her life. No, not one. . .until the Coachman had crossed her path. . .until Brin had entered her life again.

Just why she had allowed herself to fall so hopelessly in love with such a dictatorial wretch as the Coachman she couldn't imagine. But she did love him. . .as surely as she loved Brin, though with him, of course, she had refused to acknowledge what her heart had been trying to tell her for weeks. Perhaps if she hadn't stubbornly refused to admit that she was still attracted to him, that he still retained a place in her affections, she might have been able to prevent those feelings from deepening. She wasn't sure, and it hardly mattered, anyway. It was too late now. . .all too hopelessly late. She loved them both; couldn't choose between them. So how could she contemplate marriage with either one of them?

Verity came out of her heartbreaking reflections with a start when she became aware that someone was shouting her name, and swung round in the saddle to see Claud Castleford waving frantically as he came cantering across the field, mounted on his sturdy roan.

'I thought you were deliberately ignoring me,' he informed her, bringing his mount alongside and looking for all the world so much like a hurt schoolboy that she didn't hesitate to assure him that this wasn't so.

'Merely lost in my own thoughts and——' she looked about her '——lost in other ways, too. Where on earth am I? The last thing I knew I was in the Ravenhursts' wood.'

'My, my! You have been in a world of your own. You've managed to find your way on to Castleford land.' His boyish smile flashed out. 'Or it might be more accurate to say that the mare found her way here. Sarah frequently rides this way.'

'What a clever lady you are!' Verity gave the mare's silken neck a fond pat. 'Let's hope you're clever enough to find your way back.'

'Oh, I think that between us we can manage to set you on the right track. Although, if you're not in any hurry, would you like to return with me to the Grange? Or is your fiancé frantically awaiting you at Ravenhurst?'

If Claud noticed the spasm of pain flit across her features he betrayed no visible signs of having done so.
'There's no one back at the house at present. Father is
expecting a party of gentlemen later—all very hush-hush,
you understand—but there's plenty of time to show you
round the place if you would like?'

Verity accepted the invitation without a second
thought. She had liked Claud from the first. Not only was
he good-natured, but also an excellent conversationalist,
although she did find the number of times he managed
to allude to a certain young lady before they had arrived
at the Grange's stable yard a little trying, and in the
end she found herself saying in her usual no-nonsense
manner, 'For heaven's sake, Mr Castleford! If you are
so taken with Clarissa Gillingham, why on earth don't
you do something about it? How can you possibly further
your interests stuck here while she's in London? If you
take my advice you'll pack your bags and make all speed
for the metropolis!'

It took every ounce of self-control Verity possessed
to stop herself from bursting out laughing. Anyone looking at Claud's astounded expression might have supposed
that she had just suggested a visit to the other side of
the world instead of a mere short sojourn in his own
capital city.

'By gad, Miss Harcourt, you've hit on the very solution!' After dismounting, Claud offered her a helping
hand down from the saddle. 'Mama is due home the day
after tomorrow. She'll come to London if I ask her. Not
that I need her approval or support, you understand,' he
went on hurriedly as Verity looked at him rather askance,
'but squiring her about town will give me the perfect

excuse to attend those places where Miss Gillingham is likely to be found.'

Verity cast him a look of the utmost respect as she stepped into the oak-panelled hall of his ancestral home. 'Brin told me that you had hidden depths, Mr Castleford, and he wasn't wrong. Excellent strategy!'

'Did he say that?' Claud went quite pink with pleasure. 'Well, I ain't the slow-top some people take me for, Miss Harcourt, but I sometimes think it's better to keep one's own counsel about some things than to voice one's opinions and end by creating a grand fuss.'

Verity gained the distinct impression that he was referring to instances rather close to home, but steadfastly refused to pry into domestic problems which had absolutely nothing whatsoever to do with her, and focused her attention on the extremely fine interior of the early Tudor manor house.

Claud showed her into most of the downstairs rooms and ended his guided tour in the library which, like the hall, was wood-panelled, and a little gloomy, perhaps, but full of character and charmingly furnished, none the less.

'It's a wonderful old house!' Verity remarked with total sincerity. 'No wonder you're so fond of the place!'

'Yes, I am,' he freely admitted. 'It's been in the family for centuries and is steeped in history.' A rather roguish smile pulled at the corners of his not unpleasant mouth. 'The Castleford tree bears two kinds of fruit, Miss Harcourt—the good and the bad. And it has produced more than just the occasional rotten apple during its long and fertile life. The ancestor who had this house built was a prime example of the not-so-palatable. He, of course, was the one who instigated the construction of the secret passageways, so that he could spy on those invited to stay and use anything he overheard to his advantage. A most unpleasant character!'

'He sounds it,' she agreed.

'Most of the passageways were done away with when the rooms were enlarged, but the one behind here——' he tapped a section of the panelling, and it sounded hollow '——still exists. Lawrence and I discovered it when we were boys, but Father had the entrances nailed up, as you can overhear every word spoken in this room from the passageway. And there have been some very secret meetings taking place in this room in recent years, Miss Harcourt.'

Verity paid only scant attention to what he was saying as she was subjecting the panelling to a thorough examination. 'Why, one would never know there was a doorway here! It is quite remarkably well-hidden.'

'It's here.' Claud pointed to a certain section. 'If you look very closely you can just make out certain of the nails which securely fasten it. The other entrance is in Lawrence's bedchamber. That is a little easier to locate. I'll show you if you like?'

It never entered Verity's head to demur at accompanying a gentleman into a bedchamber, and, intrigued, she eagerly followed Claud up the ornately carved staircase.

'Lawrence has gone off somewhere with Father, so we're unlikely to be caught in my cousin's private sanctum,' Claud informed her as they entered the bedchamber, whose walls were also wood-panelled, but far more elaborately carved than those in either the library or the hall. 'He can be a funny devil at times—gets quite nasty if he knows someone's been in his room.'

Once again Verity only listened with half an ear as

she studied the panelling with interest. It took a little time, but eventually she noticed a slight difference in one section. 'It's here!' she said triumphantly. 'Behind this old wooden chest.'

'Very good!' Claud came across and moved the chest away from the wall. 'I wager you cannot locate the device that used to open the door, though.'

Verity didn't hesitate to take up the challenge. Each squared section had a carved rose in its centre. It had to be one of those, she decided, checking each one for any slight difference. Eventually she found one that turned beneath her inquisitive fingers. There was a faint click and a large section of the panelling opened a fraction.

'Good gad!' Claud could not have looked more stunned: his jaw dropped perceptively and his eyes widened in astonished disbelief. 'But Father had the thing nailed up years ago. Lawrence and I were here, feeling most disgruntled, when the workmen performed the task.'

He shrugged as he went over to the small table by the bedside and lit a candle. 'At least it offers me the opportunity to show you where Lawrence and I used to hide ourselves when we wanted to escape from our rather boring tutor.'

Verity smiled at this ingenuous admission as she followed him through the opening and down a series of stone steps. Footprints showed clearly in the fine covering of dust, betraying the fact that someone had certainly ventured down to the hideaway in recent years, and not someone wishful to escape a tutor, either.

The half-spiral stairway led to a narrow passageway, no more than twelve feet long by three feet wide. Three of its walls were stone-built, but the fourth was of wood. Cobwebs festooned down from the ceiling and the air was dank, but it was just the sort of place where two small boys could secrete themselves, no doubt plotting other ways to avoid lessons.

'Hello! What have we here?' Claud remarked, noticing the clearly discernible footprints at last, footprints that were far too large to be those of children. 'Someone's been down here recently.' He shrugged. 'Perhaps one of the workmen came down to check all was well and effect necessary repairs. This false wall backs on to the panelling in the library and is—'

Claud caught himself up abruptly and placed a warning finger to his lips as the door leading to the library from the hall could clearly be heard opening.

Then Lawrence Castleford's voice, bored and faintly drawling, filtered through the panelling with disturbing clarity as he said, 'I blame Claud entirely. What a complete waste of an afternoon!'

'You cannot blame him,' Lord Castleford responded. 'No doubt if we'd informed him where we were bound he'd have told us Chumley's bays were nothing more than high-steppers that would be found to be touched in the wind after no more than a mile or so. Claud might be sadly lacking in certain departments, but there ain't much the boy don't know about animals.'

Verity heard something suspiciously like a grunt before Lawrence countered with, 'Claud knew I had a fancy for those greys of his, and yet he deliberately went and offered them to Ravenhurst's damned friend.'

'He had every right to sell them to whomsoever he pleased. And you've got no cause to complain. He never objected to you making use of the turn-out whenever you were here. And you borrowed it on more than one occasion when I brought it to London.'

'He still might have offered me first refusal. I would have got the money together somehow.'

'Oh, for heaven's sake, stop whining! I've more to think about than your petty grievances!' Verity detected the chink of glass before Lord Castleford said in a milder tone, 'Here, get this down you. It'll help calm you. You do realise that you must entertain yourself this evening. Both you and Claud are barred from the library.'

'Yes, I know. Don't concern yourself. I'll find something to occupy me.'

Just what Lord Castleford would have responded to this, Verity was destined never to know, for Claud beckoned her to follow him back up the stairway.

'You are certainly in your cousin's black books,' she remarked as Claud closed the panelling and slid the chest back into position.

An unmistakable gleam of wicked satisfaction brightened his eyes as he led the way out of the room and back along the passageway to the head of the stairs. 'I cannot deny that I knew he was interested in relieving me of that turn-out, Miss Harcourt, but I also knew who would end by paying for it. Lawrence sometimes seems to have plenty of brass to throw about, but for the most part he's in debt and asking my father to bail him out.'

The front door opened and Verity checked in her descent, suddenly finding it necessary to cling to the banister-rail for support, as a stockily built figure with grizzled hair stepped into the hall. She had seen that man once before, and she recalled vividly just where she had seen him.

'Who is that?' she asked, her voice little more than a choked whisper.

'Blackmore, my cousin's manservant,' Claud

responded, watching him stalk across the hall in the direction of the kitchen area. 'He's devoted to Lawrence. Personally, I can't abide the fellow. Bit of a rum touch, if you ask me. . . Oh, confound it! Did I blow that candle out? I'd better go back and make sure. If Blackmore sees it burning he won't hesitate to inform Lawrence that someone's been in the room.'

For a few moments Verity stared sightlessly down into the hall, conjuring up clear images from the past while her mind assimilated all she had learned that day. Then, scarcely aware that Claud had left her side, she flew down the stairs and out of the house, not stopping to catch her breath until she had reached the stable yard.

Quickly mounting Sarah's mare, she galloped out of the yard and across the field in the direction of the small market town of Houghton, as though the devil himself were at her heels. So fixedly determined was she to make contact with Thomas Stone without delay, and ultimately the Coachman, that she was deaf and blind to the sights and sounds around her.

The pounding of hooves as horse and rider followed in hot pursuit went completely unnoticed, as did the hedge looming large not very far ahead, but Sarah's mare, ever alert, was only too well aware that they were getting perilously close to her particular pet hatred. Her ears went back and her eyes rolled before she took decisive and evasive action which sent her rider sailing through the air to land heavily in the ditch just in front of the offending obstacle.

Winded, and not just a little humiliated at the ease with which she had been unseated, Verity got slowly to her feet, wincing slightly as she put her weight on her right ankle.

'You faint-hearted creature!' she scolded as the mare took the precaution of moving several yards away. Then Verity at last became aware of the rider's approach and swung round, her face draining of every vestige of colour.

'Are you all right, Miss Harcourt?'

No one could have mistaken the genuine concern in Claud's voice, nor the lines of anxiety etched in his young face as he dismounted and came towards her, but Verity was suddenly alert, mistrustful, her mind whirling with hitherto unforeseen possibilities. Was it likely that Claud, too, was involved in his cousin's nefarious activities? The dreadful suspicion was swiftly quashed by common sense, coupled with age-old feminine intuition.

Placing a gentle hand beneath her arm, Claud helped her out of the shallow ditch. 'Why did you rush off that way? Was it something I said, or did?' His concern increased when he noticed her limp slightly. 'I'd better get you back to Ravenhurst.'

'No. I must go to Houghton.' Then, suddenly realising that she would be immeasurably foolish to believe herself capable of dealing with this vitally important situation on her own, she looked at him searchingly and quickly came to a decision. 'Claud, I need your help. But first there are certain things you must know and if, when you've heard me out, you choose not to help, believe me, I'll quite understand.'

Still watching him intently, Verity then went on to relate her encounter with the French spy, to inform him of her subsequent dealings with the Coachman and her meeting with Thomas Stone, and of her staunch belief that Blackmore was none other than the intermediary she had first seen at that small wayside inn.

When Claud had learned all, he uttered one word, 'Lawrence.'

'I'm so sorry,' she murmured. 'This must have come as a terrible shock to you.'

'On the contrary, Miss Harcourt, it hasn't. I've always known what a black-hearted devil Lawrence is.' His face and voice were expressionless, apathetic almost, and yet Verity knew he must be feeling something. His next words confirmed this. 'It's my father I feel sorry for. I don't know what this will do to him, but in many ways he's only himself to blame.'

He read the unspoken question in her eyes. 'Loose talk, Miss Harcourt. My father, together with many others, has known for some time that information was being passed on to the enemy. But the family always knew when these secret meetings were taking place.' He ran his fingers through his hair, suddenly looking far older than his four-and-twenty years. 'I suppose he believed he could trust his family. . . And Lawrence has always been like a son to him.

'Well, I've stood by and done nothing for long enough. I allowed Lawrence to worm his way into my father's affections at the expense of my mother and myself. I cannot prevent the dishonour his actions will bring to the family name.' Raw determination edged his voice. 'But I'll be damned if I'll sit by and let him betray his country again if I can do anything to stop him! What do you want me to do, Miss Harcourt?'

The words of comfort she wished desperately to offer were set aside by the need for urgent action. 'When is this meeting due to take place?'

'Directly after dinner, if it follows the usual pattern. And we dine early, at six. Do you want me to ride to

Houghton and see this man Stone?' he offered, but Verity shook her head.

'No, I'll do that. He knows me. He'll know I'm not spinning some yarn.'

Claud was certainly no fool, and a wry smile curled his lips. 'And, given the fact that he has no doubt been sent here for the sole purpose of keeping an eye on the members of my family, he's unlikely to listen to anything I might tell him.'

She didn't waste time attempting to deny it. 'I'm not even certain he'll be at the inn, so we must be prepared, if the worst come to the worst, to foil your cousin's attempt to pass information on to that spy ourselves.'

Verity looked up at Claud, the anxiety she felt mirrored in her eyes. Not only was she expecting him to keep a close watch on Lawrence until the authorities could be alerted, which was tantamount to placing a noose round his cousin's neck, she was asking him to place his own life in danger. But what choice had she?

'You go back to the house and try, as best you can, to act naturally. Don't attempt to keep Lawrence with you. I should imagine he usually makes some excuse to retire early when these meetings take place, so that he has ample time to secrete himself in the passageway and overhear everything that is said. If he does so this evening, then let him.'

'But how will I know if you've been successful in getting in touch with this man Stone?' he asked after a moment's intense thought.

'That's the problem, you won't. . .unless I can manage to get a message to you, or even come over myself.'

'No, don't do that. It might arouse suspicion. I'll ensure that neither Lawrence nor Blackmore leaves the house.' The muscles about his mouth grew taut. 'It's the least I can do to try to restore a little honour to our name.'

Claud offered her no opportunity to argue, and Verity could only watch, experiencing the gravest fears for his safety, as he made all speed back to the Grange. Then, without further delay, she turned and limped towards Sarah's mount, who, having regained her composure, had continued to graze quite contentedly.

She had almost reached the mare's side when the most ear-piercing, cacophonous tumult rent the air. An open carriage, tooled by someone who was incompetent, or inebriated, or both, came bowling along the road on the other side of the hedge. Sarah's mare pricked up her ears at the passengers' squeals and disharmonious attempts at singing, but when one of them suddenly attempted to play a tune on a yard of tin she wasted no time in making all speed back to Ravenhurst, and the quiet security of her stable, before Verity could make a grasp for the reins.

Chapter Sixteen

Brin cast a brief glance at Marcus's profile, and then looked blindly at the road ahead. He ought never to have agreed to accompany him out. He had been poor company, and had taken precious little interest in the fine contest they had witnessed earlier, but it would have been a grave mistake to remain at Ravenhurst with Verity.

He was not in a position to explain his behaviour now, but when he was free to do so he must somehow find a way to make her understand that not for the world would he have deliberately hurt her. He had been foolishly unthinking in his dealings with her, but not deliberately cruel.

He had believed when the time came for him to explain, to confess all, she would take it all in good spirit, as a joke; now, however, he was far from certain that her lively sense of the ridiculous would be sufficient to erase the needless hurt he had caused her; would be enough to enable her to forgive him.

'Good Gad!' Marcus ejaculated suddenly, as he noticed a rather forlorn figure emerging from a gateway a little way ahead. 'Isn't that Verity?'

Brin came out of his sombre reflections with a start and jumped down from the equipage before Marcus had brought his team to a halt. He cast one swift glance over the mud-stained habit and, before Verity could offer any explanation for her dishevelled appearance, picked her up in his arms and deposited her next to Marcus on the seat. All her protestations that she was perfectly all right, except for a sore ankle, and her requests to be taken to Houghton immediately fell on deaf ears. Marcus, trying desperately to school his features, as he had a pretty shrewd notion that hedges figured strongly in the young woman's recent misfortunes, kept his eyes glued to the road ahead, while Brin, adopting a dictatorial stance, informed her that she was going nowhere until a doctor had taken a look at her hurts.

Verity could have screamed in vexation, but there was little she could do, sandwiched as she was between two such immovable, authoritarian males, and she sat silently in ever-increasing seething frustration until they had arrived back at Ravenhurst's stable yard.

The instant Marcus had drawn his greys to a halt she called to Sutton, asking him to saddle up a fresh mount, only to have her request countermanded by Brin who, ignoring her vociferous demands to be put down at once, picked her up once more and carried her, wildly struggling, into the house.

'Oh, thank heavens, you've found her!' Sarah came rushing out to meet her husband. 'I've just this moment learned that my mare came back without her and I was about to send men out to search. Is she badly hurt? I'll go up and see what can be done.'

Marcus, his expression rather thoughtful now, placed a restraining hand on her arm. 'No, my dear. Let Brin deal with it. I rather fancy there's more to that young woman's distress than a mere sprained ankle.'

'She certainly seemed distraught over something, screaming to be put down.' A sudden smile erased her worried frown. 'But you're quite right. Brin will soon calm her. He has such a gentle way with him.'

Sarah would have been astounded had she been standing in the bedchamber a minute or so later to witness her friend taking Verity by the shoulders and shaking her so hard that the few pins remaining in her hair flew out in all directions, sending her raven locks tumbling down about her shoulders.

'Now, stop this at once!' he ordered with steel-like harshness. 'You're behaving like an unruly child!'

'Brin, you—you don't understand.' Breathless from the shaking, Verity cast a pleading glance up at his stern features. 'I must go to Houghton. It's vital I see someone there.' And even in her agitated state she could see he was suddenly very alert.

'Who?' There was no response, but Brin was not slow to note the sudden guarded look. 'You may as well get it into that pretty head of yours that you're not going anywhere, and the only person you'll be seeing, apart from Sarah, is the doctor.'

She remained stubbornly silent, and he cast her a look which not only betrayed frustration and annoyance but also managed to convey his slight feeling of hurt. 'Do you trust me so little, Verity, that you feel yourself unable to confide in me? Or is it merely that you think me incapable of acting on your behalf?'

'No, of course not! And I trust you implicitly, only—only. . .'

She slumped down on the bed, feeling utterly deflated.

The determined glint in his eyes was enough to confirm that he had no intention of allowing her to leave, and she simply didn't possess the strength to fight him any more, not even with words. The ache in her ankle was increasing and that throbbing pain had returned to her temple. Most distressing of all was the knowledge that, unless something was done quickly, poor Claud would be left to deal with a potentially dangerous situation completely alone.

So, having little choice, Verity found herself relating her dealings with the Coachman for the second time that day, and then went on to disclose what she had discovered that afternoon.

But Brin's reaction was hardly what she would have expected.

Not once did he betray the least surprise, nor even a modicum of disbelief at anything she told him and, after learning all, merely remarked rather grimly, 'So Claud Castleford is now in full possession of the facts, is he?'

She looked up at him sharply. 'Claud isn't involved. I'd stake my life on it. Why, if you could have seen his face when that doorway leading to the secret passageway opened. . .when he realised his cousin was a traitor. . . No, Brin. Claud's completely innocent.'

'I hope to God your instinct is right!' he responded, looking so forbidding that Verity hardly recognised him.

He wasted no further time and went straight over to the door. 'I'll ensure that Stone is put in the picture.' Then he paused, his hand on the doorknob, to look back at her, and flashed one of his rather wonderful smiles which managed to convey deep affection and a good deal of reassurance, too. 'Don't worry, my darling. Your Coachman won't fail you.'

No sooner had Brin left than the door opened again and Sarah entered, giving Verity no time at all to puzzle over Brin's parting words, or to concern herself with the possible happenings already taking place at Castleford Grange. It was only later, after the doctor had called and had confirmed nothing more seriously wrong than a sprained ankle and a smattering of painful bruises, and she had been left alone once again, that the gravest misgivings returned to torment her.

The draught the doctor had left to help her sleep remained untouched on the bedside table, as did the tray of food, until Meg re-entered shortly after nine o'clock to remove it. It seemed a very long time before the clock in her bedchamber chimed ten, and far longer before it chimed eleven, but when the hands were showing fifteen minutes to midnight, Verity had had enough of straining her ears, hoping to hear sounds heralding Brin's return. He hadn't returned simply because he had got himself involved. Perhaps he had been unable to make contact with Thomas Stone and had gone to the Grange to be of help to Claud. She ought to have taken that very real possibility into consideration before confiding in him. Dear God, she had put his life in danger, too!

Unable to stand the agony of waiting alone a moment longer, Verity tossed the bedcovers aside and went across to collect her robe. She was in no fit state, mentally or physically, to do anything positive herself, but at least she could talk to Marcus. Brin had the utmost respect for his friend's sound judgement, and Marcus might just be able to allay some of her worst anxieties.

There was no one in the hall, but Verity wasn't in the least surprised to discover the library door slightly ajar. Marcus wouldn't retire whilst his friend was still abroad.

After a perfunctory knock she entered to find Sarah, surprisingly, the sole occupant.

'Why, Verity!' Setting aside her sewing, Sarah went across and helped her to the chair on the opposite side of the hearth. 'The doctor assured me that draught would keep you asleep until morning.'

'I didn't take it,' Verity confessed. 'Where's Marcus?'

'He went with Brin earlier, and as yet neither of them has returned.'

'Oh, God, no!'

Sarah watched in no little concern as Verity buried her face in suddenly trembling hands. She had known the instant her husband had said that he was accompanying Brin out again, without explaining where they were going or why, that something was very wrong. The dreadful suspicion that Verity might have been attacked had crossed her mind, but during the time she had been helping Meg to bathe her young mistress and get her comfortably settled in bed in readiness for the doctor's visit this fear had thankfully been dispelled. Verity had betrayed no signs of distress whatsoever, merely deep concern over something... But what?

Moving across to the decanters, Sarah poured out two glasses of wine. 'As you refuse to take the doctor's medicine, you had better drink this, although I suspect it will go straight to your head as you didn't eat a bite of dinner. Not that I'm in any position to scold,' she added wryly. 'I didn't eat very much, either.'

She resumed her seat and stared for several moments into deeply troubled violet-blue eyes. 'Where have they gone, Verity? Do you know?'

'I suspect they are at Castleford Grange,' she responded, seeing no earthly reason to lie, and then went on to divulge what she had discovered at that lovely old manor house earlier.

'Lawrence Castleford a traitor,' Sarah murmured, betraying no surprise. 'Well, Marcus never trusted him, and I've never found his judgement faulty.'

I'm so sorry, Sarah. I've now put your husband's life in danger, too.'

'No, you haven't,' Sarah countered evenly, keeping her deepest anxieties firmly under control. 'It was Marcus's decision to accompany Brin. And I for one would not have attempted to dissuade him, even if I could.'

A proud little smile hovered about her mouth. 'Marcus has always wanted to be of service to his country during this present conflict with France. And now, of course, he has been given the opportunity to do something positive for the land of his birth. Just as you have. But how on earth did you become involved in this wretched business in the first place?'

Verity had long since come to the conclusion that Sarah Ravenhurst took a keen interest in the welfare of others, but she was neither vulgarly curious nor even moderately interfering. Whether the request stemmed from a genuine interest to learn more, or just as a means to pass the time while she waited anxiously for her husband's return, Verity wasn't sure, but because of Marcus's involvement she certainly considered that Sarah had a right to know more.

Only delaying for the time it took to make herself more comfortable in the chair, she was about to relate her dealings with the Coachman for the third time that day when she suddenly caught the sounds for which she had been longing. She sat bolt-upright again, her expression a strange mixture of joyful expectation and foreboding.

'I'll go.' Sarah had almost reached the door before Verity had time to move. 'Brin will not be best pleased to see you up at this time of night, without witnessing you hobbling about as well.'

That was the least of her worries, but Verity didn't attempt to argue. After all, Sarah was mistress in her own home, and if it was only a messenger she didn't doubt she would be apprised of any information, good or otherwise, soon enough.

Although Sarah had closed the door, the sound of voices did manage to filter into the room, but not clearly enough for Verity to discern what was being said, or by whom, but she was certain that one of the voices belonged to a man.

The door opened again and Verity, hardly daring to breathe, waited for tidings, but when only silence ensued, she rose to her feet, the glass of wine slipping from suddenly trembling fingers when she saw who it was standing with his back towards her by the door.

'Coachman. . .?' She limped several steps towards him, but he didn't attempt to turn round. 'You got my message, then?' It sounded such a foolish thing to say, but she was still in a state of shock over his unexpected appearance.

'Aye, lass.'

'Is it over. . .finally over?'

'Aye, lass.'

She limped closer. 'And Brin. . .? Marcus. . .? Are they safe?' she forced herself to ask from a throat that was suddenly dry and painful.

'Ravenhurst be wi 'is wife, lass.'

'And Brin?' There was no response, and icy talons of fear clawed at her heart. 'What's happened to him? What's happened to Brin!' Panic raised her voice almost to screaming pitch. 'Tell me, damn you!'

'Nay, then, lass. Don't tha fret thissen!' He swung round and pulled the muffler from his face. 'He's right here, my darling. . . Right here.'

Verity stared up into those wickedly twinkling tawny eyes in wonder, in disbelief, almost. For endless moments she refused to credit what her senses were telling her, had been telling her for weeks. Then anger, virulent and icy-cold, at his duplicity, at the needless, senseless hurt he had inflicted on her slowly began to well, thrusting aside every coherent thought, every need save one: a thirst for revenge.

Balling her fist, she swung her arm in a wide arc and, before Brin could take evasive action, made vicious contact with his left ear, the force of which sent that infamous tricorn sailing off his head to skid across Marcus's highly polished desk, scattering papers in its wake.

'You louse!' she screamed, and would have fled from him, but Brin had other ideas.

Pinioning her arms to her sides, he carried her back across the room and, seating himself in the chair she had just vacated, continued to hold her prisoner on his lap.

He considered she had every right to feel hurt and aggrieved, and made no attempt to stem the flow of rather colourful epithets she spat at him, most of which he suspected hadn't been learned at that very select seminary in Bath, but had been picked up by spending far too much time in the stable yard, but he did take the sensible precaution of keeping her arms securely held until, frustrated and exhausted by her ineffectual attempts to break free, she resorted to a female's most effective weapon and promptly dissolved into tears.

After forcing his handkerchief into unwilling fingers, he waited until the flow began to subside. 'I never meant to hurt you this way, my darling,' he murmured, keeping her head firmly pressed against his shoulder, while stroking the silken black locks.

'You—you have been making a May game of—of me right from the start,' she accused, regaining a little of her former spirit, and this time when she attempted to sit up he didn't try to prevent her.

'No, little one, that isn't true.' A reminiscent smile pulled at the corners of his mouth. 'Even though I made light of it, I knew from the very first time I kissed you that you were the girl for me. I told you so when we arrived in London, remember?'

The malevolent look remained, but he noticed a flicker of curiosity, too, and took heart. 'I thought it would to be a simple matter to woo you as we were both intending to spend several weeks in London, but I realised when we met in Hyde Park that day that I had grossly miscalculated, had been arrogantly presumptuous in believing my heart's desire would be mine for the asking. Why, you looked at me as though I were a leper! Of course, I realise now why you did, but at the time I was blissfully unaware that you bore a grudge against—'

'Oh, yes, very clever!' she interrupted. 'You did manage to worm a deal out of me when in the guise of the Coachman, didn't you?' She looked at him sharply and caught his rather pitiful attempt to suppress a smile, but the strong urge to box his ears soundly a second time was suppressed by rampant curiosity. 'How on earth did you manage to get back inside this room so quickly the other night?'

'It wasn't easy, I can tell you. I had only just managed to hide my tricorn and cloak in the chest in the hall and bolt the front door when I heard you attempting to enter.'

Verity didn't know whether she felt angrier with him for his duplicity, or with herself for being such a simpleton as not to have realised the truth long since.

He read her thoughts with uncanny accuracy. 'I played my part too well, but believe me it was never my intention to cause you pain.' And this time when she searched his features she could detect nothing but bitter regret.

'As the Coachman I could see you only rarely, and it was never enough. As myself I was in a position to see you much more often and was confident that, given time, you would grow fond of me again. It seemed merely a simple case of ensuring that you were given sufficient reason for seeking my company.'

Her bosom heaved. 'Infamous!'

'And in that my judgement was not at fault, as last night proved,' he continued, just as though she hadn't spoken. 'But when in my disguise I might have coped admirably at hiding my identity, but not my feelings for you, and suffered the consequences of my foolish playacting when I realised the torment I had needlessly caused. Truly, my darling, inflicting pain was not part of my plans.'

Verity could feel herself weakening, but her rapid slide into foolishly forgiving him was halted abruptly when she looked down at the fine piece of lawn in her hand, and noted with a surge of resentment that it was an exact replica of the one he had given her at Little Frampington.

'Never meant to inflict pain?' she echoed, the light of

battle returning to her eyes. 'You beat me, Brin Carter!'

His shout of laughter was hardly destined to appease, but over that particular incident he remained firm. 'You ought never to have gone to that place alone, and you know it! Although I suppose,' he added grudgingly, and in a much milder tone, 'your going did lead to the successful outcome tonight.'

This ignited more than just a spark of interest and, setting aside her justifiable grievances for the present, she asked him to explain how he had become involved.

Swiftly coming to the conclusion that it was in his own best interests to be indulgent, Brin didn't think twice about satisfying her curiosity. 'I had already sold my commission, and had been back in England nearly a month when news broke of Napoleon's escape from Elba. Wellington's own intelligence network had discovered that our little Frenchman was active again. Wellington wanted him caught and, more especially, his English contacts. He sent an urgent dispatch to Lord Charles, and suggested that he make use of my services.'

Verity recalled then that her uncle had mentioned that Wellington thought highly of Brin. 'And did you and my uncle suspect Lawrence Castleford all along?'

'Good heavens, no! We were convinced it must be someone working at the War Office, but until you saw those greys at Frampington we hadn't a clue who the traitor might be.'

He cast her a look of the utmost respect. 'Do you recall the evening of the Gillinghams' ball, when your uncle was talking to Lord Castleford? Well, it was then your uncle discovered that Castleford's nephew had been making use of that curricle and pair. We suspected that both Lord Castleford and his nephew were involved. It was also possible that Claud knew about it too. It wasn't until tonight that the truth came out. Your instincts were correct. Claud was completely innocent and Castleford hadn't a clue what his nephew had been up to.' He shook his head. 'I've never seen a man look so devastated before.'

She regarded him consideringly. 'Did you organise this sojourn at Ravenhurst simply to give you an excuse to come here so that you could keep an eye on the Grange?'

'Not entirely, no,' he admitted with a rueful smile. 'I was convinced that none of you ladies would be in the least danger, otherwise I wouldn't have arranged it. I wanted to see the thing through, of course, but I knew I'd find it difficult to keep my mind on the task if I left you behind in London. Strictly speaking, Stone was the one who was sent to keep watch. I was here merely to offer assistance if it became necessary.'

'So what happened tonight?' she prompted gently when he fell silent.

'Marcus was the only one I confided in with regard to the work I was undertaking on behalf of the government. When I related what you'd discovered, he offered his help. Like yourself, he was convinced Claud wasn't involved. So, as it would appear less suspicious if a neighbour was to call unexpectedly at the Grange, I sent him over with a message for Claud while I made contact with Stone. Marcus and I met up again later outside the Grange, but had to wait some time before Lawrence's servant came out the house. I shot Blackmore when he attempted to leave with the information.'

He sounded so matter-of-fact about it all, but then a soft-hearted approach would hardly have served his cause. Added to which, having been a soldier, shooting someone was hardly a new experience for him.

'And Lawrence?'

'No, I didn't kill him. . . Claud did. The sound of my shot alerted Lawrence and he attempted to escape, but Claud put a ball through his brain. There was no possibility of Lawrence getting away, so I assume Claud did it to save his cousin the hangman's noose. All Claud would say was that when an animal runs mad it is only humane to put it out of its misery.'

'And the French spy?'

'He's in custody.'

'So, it is finally over,' she remarked, not without a certain amount of relief.

'It will be a while before Lord Castleford gets over the revelations of this night. But for us, my darling, yes— it's over.'

He slid his arms about her narrow waist and, after the merest token resistance on her part, held her tightly to him while he contemplated the ties on her modest nightgown. 'And now, before Sarah returns, which I'm certain propriety will force her to do very shortly. . .when shall we be married?'

Verity almost choked. She wasn't sure which shocked her more: his all-too-knowing and appreciative gaze, or his arrogant assumption that she would even consider such a thing after the way he had behaved towards her.

'You've got a crass nerve to suppose that I would even contemplate marrying a perfidious wretch such as you!'

'Well, if that's the case, my girl,' he countered, making a passable attempt at appearing deeply shocked, 'all I can say is you betray a sad want of conduct. I might go as far as to say a decidedly wanton side to your nature, too, to sit on a man's lap at this time of night dressed in little more than a thin cotton nightgown, which does absolutely nothing to conceal your evident charms and which, I might add, has ridden up to reveal more than just a glimpse of pretty thighs to lead an innocent lad astray.'

Her attempts to restore a semblance of modesty were expertly foiled. Pulling her roughly against him, Brin also quickly put an end to her counter-attack on the profligate behaviour of the predatory male by kissing her so thoroughly that she was left too breathless to argue further, even had she been so inclined. Which she was not.

Although her mind might continue to suggest that it would be wise to think twice before becoming tied for life to this man whose character, she very much feared, was rather closer to that of the outrageous and domineering Coachman than the gentlemanly Major, her body was in no doubt, and neither was her heart.

Brin's gentle laughter held a note of triumph as he held her away. 'I rather think after that response, my darling, you would be foolish even to attempt to resist your destiny.'

Verity couldn't prevent a rather wistful little smile at this, as she nestled herself more comfortably into the crook of her future husband's arm, because it was no more than she had been telling herself for weeks.

Perhaps she had been destined to take a seat on that mail-coach that day and, yes, perhaps destiny had decreed years ago that she would one day be tied irrevocably to this man. And who was she to argue with destiny? she mused, while at the same time thinking she was rather foolish to allow him to get away with his outrageous behaviour towards her so easily, and she found herself saying, but without any degree of conviction, 'You do realise that if you become riveted to me, Major Coachman Carter, you will live under the cat's foot. I think it only fair to warn you that I'll rule the roost with a rod of iron.'

'Don't tha fret thissen, lass,' he responded, looking highly delighted at the prospect. 'I'd 'ave to be a right dunderheead not to 'ave realised that long since.'

Verity, raising her eyes heavenwards, thought that Lady Billington hadn't been far wrong when she had suggested there was a streak of insanity in the Harcourt family. Why else would anyone even consider becoming tied to such a reprehensible creature?

4 FREE
books and a surprise gift!

We would like to take this opportunity to thank you for reading this Mills & Boon® book by offering you the chance to take FOUR more specially selected titles from the Historical Romance™ series absolutely FREE! We're also making this offer to introduce you to the benefits of the Reader Service™—

- ★ FREE home delivery
- ★ FREE gifts and competitions
- ★ FREE monthly newsletter
- ★ Books available before they're in the shops
- ★ Exclusive Reader Service discounts

Accepting these FREE books and gift places you under no obligation to buy, you may cancel at any time, even after receiving your free shipment. Simply complete your details below and return the entire page to the address below. *You don't even need a stamp!*

YES! Please send me 4 free Historical Romance books and a surprise gift. I understand that unless you hear from me, I will receive 4 superb new titles every month for just £2.99 each, postage and packing free. I am under no obligation to purchase any books and may cancel my subscription at any time. The free books and gift will be mine to keep in any case.

H8XE

Ms/Mrs/Miss/Mr.................................Initials ....
BLOCK CAPITALS PLEASE

Surname ....

Address ....

....

....Postcode..................................

Send this whole page to:
THE READER SERVICE, FREEPOST, CROYDON, CR9 3WZ
(Eire readers please send coupon to: P.O. BOX 4546, DUBLIN 24.)

Historical Romance is being used as a trademark.

Historical Romance™

Coming next month

THE MERRY GENTLEMAN
by Meg Alexander

Part two of this exciting Regency trilogy:
Perry's story

With danger of attack imminent from the French
Perry is aghast to find Elizabeth stowing away
aboard ship. It is all he can do to keep her safe,
but then why does he care? It's not *even* as if he
likes her, is it?

THE KING'S NEW MAN
by Elizabeth Henshall

A medieval pageantry! Book three in the series

Maude was forced to spy on William de Rohan
by the man who held her brother captive. Getting
close to de Rohan, Maude realised that she was
faced with the choice of betraying her brother—or
the man she loves.

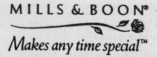

MILLS & BOON®

Makes any time special™

On sale from 1st June 1998